Climate Positi

This is the decade for climate action. Internal and external stakeholders demand action. How we choose to act in the next ten years will determine our foreseeable future.

Businesses hold a critical role for climate futures. The need for businesses to reduce their carbon footprint is now unquestioned, but how to achieve reductions in a credible way is neither clear nor easy once you've tackled the obvious energy culprits. *Climate Positive Business* lays out the path of business climate strategy, highlighting how your business must set goals, measure impact, and improve performance.

Greenhouse gas protocols can instruct you on the core accounting process that lies at the heart of climate strategy. At least as important to success are the details that protocols don't tell you: the sticking points, the areas of controversy, and the best practices.

Rooted in real experience and written in an entertaining and engaging style, this book provides you with the tips, tools, and techniques to tackle your company's carbon footprint, and it helps you do so in a way that is credible and appropriately ambitious to meet stakeholder expectations. The book will equip you with tools to think critically about GHG reduction, carbon offsets, and carbon removal, as well as help ensure we collectively implement real solutions to slow and eventually reverse the climate crisis. It includes lessons learned from real-world consulting projects and provides a plan of action for readers to implement.

A go-to book for businesses looking to understand, manage, and reduce their carbon footprint, it is an invaluable resource for sustainable business practitioners, consultants, and those aspiring to become climate champions.

David Jaber is the founder and CEO of Climate Positive Consulting, a firm that advances better decision-making through climate strategy, carbon footprint analysis, and greenhouse gas reduction. Over the last 20 years, David has worked with over 150 companies on environmental excellence.

"Impressive in its breadth, thoughtfulness, and pragmatism, *Climate Positive Business* offers a perspective and a plan of action from someone who's been in the trenches, on the front lines, for decades."

— Gil Friend, Founder and CEO of Natural Logic;
Founder, Critical Path Capital; International Society
of Sustainability Professionals Hall of Famer

"Want an easy-to-understand, how-to-guide to go climate positive? Read this book, as David Jaber explains why, shows how, and adds in humor along the way, based on his years of expertise, and real-life implementations to build a better world."

— R. Paul Herman, CEO, HIP Investor
Ratings + Portfolios; co-editor and co-author,
The Global Handbook of Impact Investing

"Given the urgency of climate change, business and organizational leaders are called to create climate action plans. But where to start? What's a science-based target? What the heck are Scope 1, 2, and 3? *Climate Positive Business* is a clear guide to help businesses understand how to measure, report, and reduce their carbon footprints, whether they're making their own plans or hiring a consultant. Jaber provides an overview along with the details. There's no time to waste; let's start global cooling!"

— Elysa Hammond, SVP, Environmental
Stewardship, Clif Bar & Company

Climate Positive Business

How You and Your Company Hit Bold Climate Goals and Go Net Zero

David Jaber

LONDON AND NEW YORK

First published 2022
by Routledge
2 Park Square, Milton Park, Abingdon, Oxon OX14 4RN

and by Routledge
605 Third Avenue, New York, NY 10158

Routledge is an imprint of the Taylor & Francis Group, an informa business

British Library Cataloguing-in-Publication Data
A catalogue record for this book is available from the British Library

Library of Congress Cataloging-in-Publication Data
Names: Jaber, David, 1972– author.
Title: Climate positive business : how you and your company
hit bold climate goals and go net zero / David Jaber.
Description: Milton Park, Abingdon, Oxon ;
New York, NY : Routledge, 2022. | Includes
bibliographical references and index. |
Identifiers: LCCN 2021014788 | ISBN 9781032043432
(hardback) | ISBN 9781032043449 (paperback)
Subjects: LCSH: Social responsibility of business. |
Environmental protection—Economic aspects. |
Climate change mitigation.
Classification: LCC HD60 .J329 2022 | DDC 658.4/083—dc23
LC record available at https://lccn.loc.gov/2021014788

ISBN: 978-1-032-04343-2 (hbk)
ISBN: 978-1-032-04344-9 (pbk)
ISBN: 978-1-003-19154-4 (ebk)

DOI: 10.4324/9781003191544

Typeset in Bembo
by codeMantra

Contents

About the author

David Jaber is the Founder of Climate Positive Consulting (www.climatepositiveconsulting.com), a firm that advances better decision-making through climate strategy, carbon footprint analytics, and greenhouse gas reduction. Over the course of 20 years, David has worked with over 150 companies to help them advance environmental excellence. He is a B Corporation owner (www.bcorporation.net), a Project Drawdown Fellow (www.drawdown.org), and an advocate with the American Sustainable Business Council (www.asbcouncil.org). David holds two degrees in engineering from Rice University and U.C. Berkeley, and lives with his spouse, plants and a laptop on Costanoan Ohlone lands in the San Francisco Bay Area.

Foreword

by Joel Makower
Chairman and Executive Editor, GreenBiz Group

It's fashionable these days to talk about tipping points, inflection points, disruption, resets, and pivots. What all of them, individually and collectively, reflect is this moment of great uncertainty, of unprecedented change, of enormous challenges and unparalleled opportunities. The news cycles are dizzying, and almost everything seems up for grabs.

It can be scary, to be sure, but also exhilarating. After all, when everything is changing, anything is possible. The chance to reinvent business and commerce to operate within the boundaries of a finite planet, the ability to envision a fairer economy, the chance to rethink the role of companies in society, the opportunity to birth a new generation of social entrepreneurs—it's an exciting time.

Those of us who have worked for decades in sustainable business have seen this coming for a while. We've watched the impacts of climate change moving ever closer—slowly at first, then not-so-slowly—as well as a raft of other environmental and social challenges that are rattling our economy and spurring companies to react. We see danger, but also opportunity.

Working in sustainability is an inherently optimistic, can-do profession. We show up every day with a vision of a positive future and a better world, and we work to develop and share ideas about how we'll get there. We talk about moonshots, about bold, audacious goals. We avoid incrementalism, knowing that it's necessary but insufficient to meet tomorrow's challenges at the scale, scope, and speed required to address them.

At the same time, we're pragmatists. Sure, the ideal of a sustainable planet and regenerative businesses is compelling, and it can feel starry-eyed to envision a world where the way companies operate actually restores, or at least doesn't deplete, the natural capital upon which our economy—indeed, all life—depends. Is it idealistic to imagine that companies can be a positive force in society, creating not just economic wealth but also ensuring the well-being of all living things? If so, count me in.

The upshot of all this is that society has been flipping the script when it comes to the conversation about business and the planet, and particularly about the climate. It's no longer just "What is business doing to harm the climate?" It's also "What is a changing climate doing to harm business?" The answers, companies are finding, have potentially staggering implications for productivity and profits in the coming years.

And yet there is plenty to celebrate these days. Though it may not be widely reported by the mainstream media, there is a revolution taking place in business, one where many of the world's largest companies are rethinking and redesigning their products and services in a way that hews to the vision and spirit of the United Nations Sustainable Development Goals. A revolution where companies are redesigning products and packaging to keep their constituent materials in play endlessly. Where powering the planet doesn't mean warming it to dangerous levels. Where access to life's necessities—healthy and affordable food, clean water, reliably clean energy, affordable and accessible transportation—is within reach.

The headlines are full of such stories, if you know where to look. The world's largest retailer plans to eliminate its carbon footprint in two decades. The world's Big Four accounting firms have come together to devise a set of common metrics on how to assess companies on sustainability. Scores of companies have pledged to be "carbon negative"—taking more greenhouse gases from the atmosphere than they emit—or to zero out their extractions of water from the earth by ensuring its replacement. These and many others provide hope and inspiration.

Of course, all of this is easy to say, but extraordinarily hard to do. It takes high-level corporate commitment, metrics, communications, partnership, and, inevitably, plowing new ground. It is complicated stuff. It demands understanding biology, physics, and chemistry, not to mention finance.

So, what will it take for more companies to lean into this moment? The answer lies within these pages. David Jaber deftly taps into his own decades of firsthand experience working with a wide range of companies. He offers the kind of knowledge, insights, and counsel to get the job done.

As Jaber makes clear, the time for incrementalism is over. It's time for bold goals. There is much to do, opportunities to seize, new business models to scale, and precious little time to get it done. We're already experiencing the unthinkable: more wildfires, floods, droughts, hurricanes, tornadoes, and all the other manifestations of a planet under stress.

But it's not hopeless, as this book makes clear. The solutions exist. The leaders are showing the way. The answers are known.

The key, as always, is asking the right questions.

Acknowledgments

This book would not have been possible without the clients over the past 15+ years who brought me into their carbon footprint explorations and grappled with how to do business better. To their efforts, appreciation is due.

I would like to acknowledge the organizations and individuals who allowed me to use their images to better relate this story, and whose names are listed as the source of each figure. I thank the greater Creative Commons community for generously making their work available. Thank you to the team at Routledge—Rebecca Marsh, Kelly Cracknell, Sophie Peoples and Rajamalar—and parent company Taylor and Francis Group for working with me to broadcast this work, and keeping the faith that we'd get through the process.

Deserving of individual recognition are Leslie Jackson for her editorial support; Joel Makower for graciously writing a foreword; Gil Friend, R. Paul Herman, and Elysa Hammond for graciously providing testimonials; and Donya Saied for her all-around support. I am also indebted to key colleagues, friends, and family members for their unwavering belief in the direction of this effort.

Let me recognize Project Drawdown, whose inspirational analysis validates multiple positions held in this writing. Recognition is also due to the GHG Protocol and the Science Based Targets Initiative. In their genesis lie the seeds of this book.

Introduction

> We no sooner get a problem solved than we are overwhelmed
> with a multiplicity of additional problems in a most beautiful
> payoff of heretofore unknown, previously unrecognized, and
> as-yet unsolved problems.
>
> – R. Buckminster Fuller

The call from customers, communities, and a diverse range of
stakeholders is clear. You and your business must make progress
on climate fronts. How you can and will make progress is seldom
clear when first embarking on the climate path. I am here to serve
as your guide. My intent is to provide you with insights on the
process, tools for you and your business to succeed, and pathways
to help you avoid setbacks and pitfalls.

As you make progress, you also want to avoid creating new problems in the course of solving old problems. I'm often reminded that
good intentions can have unintended consequences. One example
is in the case of Parchment, MI.

The origins of Parchment, MI go back to 1909 with the found-
ing of the Kalamazoo Vegetable Parchment Company, established
in an old sugar beet factory along the Kalamazoo River.[1] The plant
produced paper for not only food protection, but also printing and
other specialty uses. Its presence led to the establishment of the
Village of Parchment and, shortly thereafter, the City. Early his-
torians note the smooth working government and how it had a
"splendid water system" supplied by deep wells.[2] Over the decades, Parchment continued to attract other companies connected

DOI: 10.4324/9781003191544-1

with the paper industry. Fort James Corporation, which took over papermaking operations in the City in 1995, was acquired by national papermaker Georgia Pacific in 2000.

In 2018, it was discovered that elevated levels of per- and poly-fluorylalkyl substances (PFAS) were in Parchment's drinking water, 26 times the federal advisory level.[3] PFAS are used to manufacture water- and grease-resistant products. PFAS have been popularized by the movie *Dark Waters* and are also referred to as "forever chemicals," as they don't break down and are found not only in our waterways, but in our bodies.[4] Some community members took issue with the heightened chemical exposure, sweeping up Georgia Pacific, suspected of using PFAS in paper treatment, and 3M, which used to make PFAS-containing chemicals used by at least one local company, in a lawsuit.[5]

Chemicals like PFAS are a specific example illustrating a general pattern. We often develop and design products to drive improvements: better water resistance, better adhesion, improved water repellent qualities, better energy efficiency, lower air pollution, etc. Those products often solve that problem spectacularly well. However, new problems emerge in employing those solutions, like the water pollution of PFAS, the mercury hazards of fluorescent bulbs, or the question of how to recycle solar panels at end of life.

Parchment's story serves as a cautionary note to businesses to know the impacts that their products and services have on their surroundings, whether those impacts are on water, climate, workers, or the greater community. If it's true you can't *manage* what you don't measure in your business, it's clearly true that you can *mangle* what you don't measure. Measurement raises your awareness around any mangling, enables action before the lawsuits come, and helps you avoid the broadside of someone else's unwelcome discovery. Measurement also allows you to judge whether you've succeeded beyond your wildest expectations. Where measurement does identify that we have created new problems, we need to gauge the magnitude of new problems vis-à-vis the old problems that we are solving, and assess how easy new problems are to solve.

Measurement can be as simple as a glimpse of an R&D experiment to see that it's not developing in the right way, the obvious failure of a piece of equipment, or the lack of results from the software code you're writing. For actions where the results are not quite so apparent, like reducing greenhouse gas (GHG) emissions, measurements become more labor- and time-intensive. Even if we put in that time and labor, sometimes what we *think* we need to measure isn't actually *what* we need to measure. For example, one of the many areas of business climate impact is waste management. In measuring the success of waste reduction programs, diversion rate is often used as a measure, looking at how much of the material flowing out of a business goes to recycling or compost, rather than landfill or incineration. If you're successful on the diversion front, it's possible that a process improvement to truly benefit the company, like going paperless, will hurt your diversion rate, as the paper you were recycling is suddenly gone. If your purpose was to always increase diversion, you'd lobby against going paperless. (Solution: use tons of waste to landfill as your measure rather than diversion rate, as long as your diversion rate is 80+%, and drive down tons to landfill. Paperless people are happy and waste diverters are happy.)

Climate is often framed as a single issue, but it is multifaceted, touching on virtually all aspects of our operations and our lives. Climate impact is tightly bound to the systems we currently have that make so much of economy and lifestyle possible. Taking responsibility for those impacts is necessarily a huge portion of "sustainable business" effort, and sustainable business has been around as a term and topic for over 20 years. These days, people who are too cool for sustainability school might use the term "regenerative," and if regenerative holds additional nuance in how your business relates to its surroundings, I would yet consider them the same thing—ensuring our businesses, and all the systems on which they depend, survive and thrive into the indefinite future.

The perspectives we hold on how to tackle climate problems are tailored . . . and inspired . . . and circumscribed . . . by the role(s) we play. My role has been to serve as a consultant, quantifying the benefits and impacts of business actions, analyzing footprints, and helping clients answer key questions:

- How much climate-stressing GHGs are we emitting?
- What are our pathways to reduce undesired impacts?
- What is our strategy to embed those pathways in business operations?

- What are our opportunities to create real improvements for ecology, commerce, and workforce in implementing this strategy?
- How do we as teams, with our collective variety of roles, push forward on implementation?

If your goal is to troubleshoot undesired climate impacts—whether as an internal company agent or an external advisor—then you need the ability to see the components of global systems as well as the risks and opportunities that climate-related trends pose to businesses, communities, and governments. At its best, troubleshooting climate problems is analytical, taking a data- and fact-based approach to understanding the relationships between market, business, and supply chain impacts. And as good troubleshooters, we understand the crucial role that we as individuals have to play, in our mindset, our leadership styles, our ability to understand what motivates others, our ability to create projects and spaces that allow people to excel, and the beliefs that we choose to hold.

Understanding trends and systems is necessary but not sufficient. For you to be successful on climate fronts, you will also need to:

- Craft bold climate strategy
- Implement the strategy, applying tips, tools, and best practices
- Avoid pitfalls by learning from the lessons of others

The profit motive—or at least the motive to thrive while providing a needed good or service—is the force that keeps businesses in business. Rather than have climate and profit be oppositional—as has so often been the case in the past, because of inadequate business strategy—we need to harmonize. The path to profit must go through dramatic climate action.

Many larger companies are working on that harmonization, with leadership channeling resources into strategies and projects. Companies that have set or committed to set bold climate goals include PepsiCo, Tyson Foods, Kimberly-Clark, Procter & Gamble, Whirlpool, Microsoft, Wal-Mart, Nike, Esteé Lauder, General Mills, and over 1,500 other major brands. Those in their supply chain must follow. Businesses must be responsive to the evolution driven by consumer preference, enlightened investors, and the understanding of science.

Many observations and experiences are captured in this book to support that quest.

- Trends that influence the business climate trajectory are highlighted in the "Evolve with the Business Landscape" chapter, which features guideposts that should factor into your business climate strategy.
- The core process of quantifying GHGs and setting climate targets is in the "Block and Tackle Your Climate Strategy" chapter, providing the overview on scopes, emission factors, and setting targets. It also offers viewpoints on measurement as it relates to supporting you—or not supporting you—in achieving your goals. If you are steeped in GHG accounting, feel free to skip the first portion of the section, but my anticipation is that you will find value in the discussion of details.
- Once you've quantified your GHG footprint, you then look at options for GHG footprint reduction to hit those climate targets. Those options are covered in the "Reduce GHG! The Saga Continues" chapter.
- Areas of controversy are covered in the "Choose Wisely" chapter, which outlines two arenas in which we either get mixed signals around what's good and what's bad, or the best path forward simply isn't clear, even without mixed signals. This chapter provides an attempt to make sense of the dissonance.
- After you've had success, or have made at least enough progress to start making claims, the "Seek the Truth and It Shall Set You Free" chapter covers considerations for communication and claims. The "Consider More Than Carbon" chapter highlights several related issues that are relevant to your business strategy, and illustrates the interconnections among issues.
- Finally, the plan of action to move forward is encapsulated in the "Pull It All Together" chapter.

Note that I will use "carbon footprint," "greenhouse gas emissions," and "greenhouse gas (GHG) footprint" interchangeably, all signifying a company's impact on the climate. Note also that the business climate field is evolving quickly. The area of science-based targets (SBTs), which takes much of my focus here, was barely around four years ago, and companies are already looking beyond SBTs to longer-term net zero goals. I've incorporated the latest material to be current up to the publication date. Additionally, even if many of the details are evolving, the core process of tackling your GHG footprint is relatively static. Many businesses are now committing to the core process for the next ten years and beyond. Ultimately, my hope for you is that you find tools, trends, tips, and techniques to help you move forward on your business climate strategy and gain the ability to join the leading companies, should you choose to do so. Understanding the fundamentals offered in this book will support you in navigating the future evolution in the field.

Let's begin!

Notes

1 Parchment Community Library, "Parchment History", Parchment Community Library, 2020. https://www.parchmentlibrary.org/local-history
2 Author unknown, *History of Parchment*, 1933. https://3c87a426-5e6d-4082-a7bc-25165b670f4f.filesusr.com/ugd/53126d_73921f4689794317b1900bd0c50588b5.pdf
3 Brad Devereaux, "Concerns Remain a Year after Parchment Learned of Toxic PFAS in Its Water", MLive Media Group, July 24, 2019. https://www.mlive.com/news/kalamazoo/2019/07/concerns-remain-a-year-after-parchment-learned-of-toxic-pfas-in-its-water.html
4 Rebecca Hersher, "Scientists Dig into Hard Questions about the Fluorinated Pollutants Known As PFAS", NPR, April 22, 2019. https://www.npr.org/sections/health-shots/2019/04/22/708863848/scientists-dig-into-hard-questions-about-the-fluorinated-pollutants-known-as-pfa
5 Malachi Barrett, "Lawsuit alleges 3M and Georgia-Pacific caused Parchment PFAS emergency", MLive Media Group, January 29, 2019. https://www.mlive.com/news/kalamazoo/2018/11/3m_and_georgia-pacific_sued_fo.html

Chapter 1

Evolve with the business landscape

> Focus on contribution to the larger good—and the needs of the decision-maker—not just the achievement of your objectives.
> – Marshall Goldsmith, leadership coach and business author

Koyaanisqatsi is the Hopi word for "life out of balance," highlighted in the 1980s by director Godfrey Reggio in his film of that name. It is telling that we do not have just a single word in English to simply convey that same sense, as life out of balance is the situation in which many English speakers find themselves today. If life is out of balance, then the business landscape is out of balance, too.

If you're reading this, you're likely already attuned to the environmental crises of which plenty has been written. Let me cut to the chase.

Businesses need to be responsive to their social and ecological surroundings of which they are part, maintain healthy practices, and innovate where practices are less healthy. The good news is that many industries have made strides in better directions—investing in renewable energy, launching product lines with improved material choices, and tackling their environmental footprint. But the effort has not been anywhere near requisite to our challenge.

This is the reason we have sustainability-oriented job positions and a climate consulting industry. If business as usual didn't create problems, in theory, we would not need people to help mitigate those problems. Also, in theory, as climate practitioners, we are trying to work ourselves out of jobs, by embedding better practices

DOI: 10.4324/9781003191544-2

into business operations and making stand-alone sustainability positions irrelevant. However, impacts are a matter of degree, not either/or, and embedding better practices is a process, not an end state. I suspect we'll need people to monitor trends, measure impacts, manage certifications, engage employees, and reduce emissions for a long time.

To reiterate, for you to be successful on climate fronts, you will need to:

• Craft bold climate strategy
• Implement the strategy, applying tips, tools, and best practices
• Avoid pitfalls by learning from the lessons of others

Before delving into climate specifics, though, it's important to understand the context of the trends in policy, markets, ecosystems, technologies, and customer preferences that are connected to business climate strategy. There are many themes among those business trends: international goals, business organizational standards, reporting, purchasing practices, sustainable water use, non-toxic materials, and diversity/inclusion. Let's touch on them at least in brief.

20/20 vision for the 2020s

> Successful business leaders must evolve a much more expansive view of time . . . One way to expand your thinking is to look to the UN Sustainable Development Goals, whose time horizon is 2030 . . . think of them as a purchase order from the future.
> – John Elkington, author and corporate responsibility authority

Vision is crucially important in business. Vision sets the frame for the initiatives and goals by which our success is assessed. Vision is the frame around our day-to-day activity.

Multiple frameworks for an internationally accepted vision have been developed over the years to help guide actions across the globe. Out of an effort to craft a vision around the role of business, The Natural Step (TNS) movement was born nearly 30 years ago. TNS was an international network of stakeholders, charting out how businesses, communities, and nations could best align with the ge-ology, hydrology, ecology, and atmospheric science of the planet.

TNS came up with four clear principles:

We must strive to use 100% renewable resources.
We must strive to use 100% non-toxic materials.
We must maintain the productivity of the earth's living systems.
Resources must be used fairly and efficiently to meet human needs.

There is a readily understandable logic behind these principles:

Renewable: If resources are non-renewable, then by definition, they won't be available for the future, and their use at an un-sustainable rate hinders future generations.

Non-Toxic: If materials are toxic, then by definition, they are harming life.

Abundant: If we are hindering the ability of living systems to be productive, we're increasing the risk that their yield won't be available to sustain life.

Equitable: If we exacerbate inequity, we risk immigration pres-sures, unrest, rebellion, and invasion where peoples aren't able to meet their basic needs.

TNS was very influential in the mid- to late 1990s among many of the people who came to characterize sustainability consulting as a profession. I'm not going to drop names, but you know who you are.

If not top of mind often these days, the general direction of the TNS principles has been broadly validated by billions of people. On September 25, 2015, the United Nations adopted 17 Sustainable Development Goals (SDGs) to "end poverty, protect the planet, and ensure prosperity for all" by 2030, building on the eight Millen-nium Development Goals set in 2000.

All 17 goals are highlighted in Figure 1.1. In addition to stress-ing clean water, clean energy, and healthy life on land and sea, the SDGs emphasize social equity.

- No Poverty
- Zero Hunger

Figure 1.1 UN SDG Chart.
Source: United Nations.

- Good Health (maternal survival, epidemic reduction, road traffic safety)
- Quality Education (access to primary, secondary, and university education; vocational and technical skills)
- Gender Equality (equal rights, pay, access to resources)
- Access to Clean Water (sufficient for quality of life)
- Access to Affordable and Clean Energy (energy to provide quality of life, while not hindering quality of life elsewhere)
- Decent Work and Economy (economic growth in least developed countries, improved global resource efficiency)
- Reduced Inequality within and among Countries (higher income growth in the bottom 40%, reduced discrimination policy, orderly migration)
- Peace and Justice (free of war, just rule of law)

The SDGs, like TNS, provide a model framework for results whether you're an external sustainability consultant, internal company staff, or involved in non-profit, philanthropic, or academic endeavors.

If in the United States we were measuring ourselves against SDG goals, we would see that we have much to do. It's not simply an exercise for the developing world, as in the international contest, we're in 31st place(!), according to the Sustainable Development Report,[1] the global study that shows where each nation stands on SDG implementation! The thirty-first place for the United States would never happen in an Olympics contest. Yet, here we are.

The question many businesses face, in considering how to contribute, is: how are SDGs relevant? As a business, you might not directly impact transboundary integrated water resources management or the poverty rate of your nation. But you can pay living wage. You can donate to poverty alleviation and workforce development efforts. There are ways to work with SDGs, and smart companies are figuring out those ways.

Given there are 17 goals with 169 targets, it is admittedly a little overwhelming. The key is to identify those that are most relevant to your business. If you're a seafood restaurant chain, Life Under Sea is a logical choice. If you're teaching STEM skills to girls, Gender Equity is well aligned.

In addition to vision, implementation is crucial. "Vision without execution is hallucination" is a quote attributed to people ranging from Thomas Edison to Steve Case. Without translation of a vision into clear actions, you'll remain in the realm of delirium. As it turns out, there are structures and standards developed specifically for businesses that help address the SDG spectrum of issues.

Have some standards

> People should have values. Companies are nothing more than a collection of people . . . by extension, all companies should have values.
>
> – Tim Cook, CEO of Apple

If you believe you should have standards in some relationships in your life, you should have standards for your business relationships, too. Certain standards are required by the government, yet many important standards are instead adopted voluntarily after an informed review of a business challenge.

The B Corporation standard is a standard for responsibility that predated the SDGs. B Corporation is similar to TNS and the SDGs by providing a holistic framework as outlined in Figure 1.2, but different in serving as a business-specific standard rather than an international model. Even if the broad TNS principles can be applied to business, B Corporation gets into details that are more readily incorporated by businesses.

As much as I hear about B Corporations, I'm often surprised that there are only 4,000+ of them currently in the world, less than 0.001% of all businesses. B Corporations tend to be smaller businesses, as the governance requirements can be challenging for publicly traded companies, even if a few companies like Danone and Etsy have proven a publicly traded B Corporation is not a complete unicorn. You join the B Corp club by scoring 80 or more on the 200-point B Impact Assessment (BIA). Additional requirements may be added in the near-term, but that's the key threshold for now. Note the self-assessment involved in the BIA requires you to provide

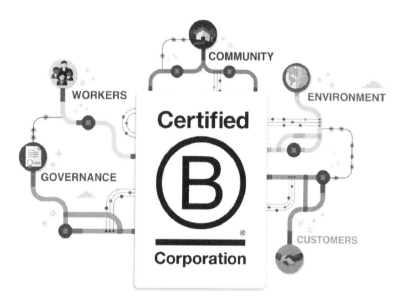

Figure 1.2 B Corp Logo.
Source: B Lab, bcorporation.net.

Figure 1.3a B Corp Environment.
Source: B Lab, bcorporation.net.

Figure 1.3b B Corp Customers.
Source: B Lab, bcorporation.net.

Figure 1.4a B Corp Community.
Source: B Lab, bcorporation.net.

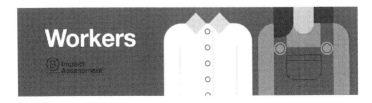

Figure 1.4b B Corp Workers.
Source: B Lab, bcorporation.net.

Figure 1.4c B Corp Governance.
Source: B Lab, bcorporation.net.

documentation, run numbers, and formalize policies in what is generally a process of several months, including cycles of review by B Corporation support staff.

To be a successful B Corporation, you must prove good practice in the areas of governance, worker care, community, customers, and the environment, as depicted in Figures 1.3 and 1.4. Good practice is inclusive of climate strategy and climate action.

As good as B Corporations are, you can go further. Enter LIFT Economy, a consulting firm whose mission is "for the benefit of all life." I have been watching LIFT for years, and I have appreciated their thought leadership around how a business should operate in service of that mission. Elements they encourage to build upon a B Corp baseline include the following:

- Need-Oriented Products and Services. The COVID-19 pandemic was a lesson in the resilience of providing "essential services" and meeting core needs. If your offering is not essential, you're at risk of being shut down. With B Corporations, you do need to show benefits of your products and services, but the Assessment as a standard doesn't explicitly require need-oriented goods and services. The difference is in providing products and services for which there is a real need, rather than optional products that happen to find willing buyers, like manufacturing small umbrellas for exotic drinks. Defining "need" is certainly nuanced, and different people can have different yet valid answers. If someone chooses to buy something, it suggests they have a need, but products that are cosmetic or ornamental are less connected to what are generally considered basic needs, and addictive products drive you to buy them even when part of you knows it's not wise to do so. It's beneficial for company owners to think through what they are actually offering to the world.

- Equitable Democratic Culture. You can have a centrally controlled B Corporation with one or a few people getting all the profit. Yes, owners take on more risk, and reward should reflect that, but you can choose to allow everyone to have the opportunity to become an owner, whether full ownership through cooperative models or milder forms of ownership like employee stock ownership programs (ESOPs). There is an increased recognition of the value of democratically controlled businesses, where if all contribute toward success, all should benefit. Related to equitable culture are rules like maximum pay ratios between the lowest paid and highest paid employees.

- Open Source/Transparent. If we're truly seeking to maximize benefit, and we've come up with something that creates benefits, there's greater social value in making it open source. This flies in the face of an intellectual property mindset. We should certainly be judicious in what information we share, and not share the information that has a critical role for the success and well-being of our businesses. In this moment, the pendulum of corporate information management swings in the direction of secrecy and non-sharing, which suggests we have the capacity to be more open. There can be real value in helping the resilience of your sector by sharing useful processes and procedures that lie outside of what you consider your competitive advantage.

- Support of Local Economy Ecosystem. Localization techniques, like finding suppliers within 50 or 150 miles of your facility, can help minimize the impacts of your supply chain and maximize the benefits to the communities to which you're most closely connected. To the extent you are significantly affected by prosperity and stability in your local community, it makes sense to support that prosperity through your business activity.

In addition to B Corporations, a parallel development with larger, publicly traded companies is the rise of "stakeholder capitalism," where companies take into account the broader needs of employees, suppliers, customers and communities in business decision-making. Stakeholder capitalism contrasts with shareholder capitalism, which has dominated business governance thought for decades, and has posited that the sole purpose of publicly traded business is to generate returns to shareholders. Though we've seen strains of the stakeholder capitalism movement for decades in shareholder action groups and beyond, stakeholder capitalism received an injection of energy through a recent statement from the Business Roundtable, a coalition of CEOs that has historically followed the shareholder view on the role of business in society. In 2019, in "redefining the purpose of the corporation," they acknowledged that successful businesses must take a broader view on their impacts in the greater world.[2] They almost certainly came to this view because of the actions and mandates from more proactive business groups as well as stakeholders.

A factor in governance that drives companies to stakeholder capitalism is the investor community and investor pressure. Many point to letters from Larry Fink, CEO of BlackRock, the world's largest private asset manager, and his exhortations for business to take a broader view, as an indicator that the tide has turned. In 2020, he announced "the evidence on climate risk is compelling investors to reassess core assumptions about modern finance," signaling that they would remove companies that generate more than 25% of revenues from coal production from their actively managed portfolios.[3] His 2021 letter notes that "no issue ranks higher than climate change on our clients' lists of priorities" and that we know "climate risk is investment risk." It goes further to state that businesses with a clear strategy for net zero GHG emissions will distinguish themselves, and those that don't will lose the confidence of stakeholders.[4] Critics point out that BlackRock itself does not always live up to these principles, with entire campaigns focused on pressuring BlackRock to discontinue investing in fossil fuels,[5] but nevertheless to have that messaging coming from someone in Larry's position is welcome.

It is interesting to note that the concerns raised by Mr. Fink primarily address the infrastructure, insurance, and other disruption caused by the climate crisis. Those of us who have been working on the mitigation front for years have done so precisely to try and avoid these negative impacts. Unfortunately, we now see enough costly incidents and economic disruption to trigger organizations like BlackRock to take action. The preferred scenario would have involved foresight among the BlackRocks and Business Roundtables of the world to take the early action that others had advocated for, rather than wait—as we have—for the climate crisis to escalate. Certainly, those benefiting the most from the existing system are the least likely to change it. However, those who hold power should be attuned to greater market forces, as there is plenty of profit potential in more responsible paths for those who seek it.

Additional pressure from the investment community comes in the form of ESG investing (environment, society, and governance). Bloomberg reports $30 trillion in assets are invested with ESG-related criteria.[6] ESG investing requires transparency from companies around ESG-related efforts, and that requirement has driven the development of organizations like the Value Reporting Foundation, which has developed standards for corporate disclosure. If your day job hasn't revolved around corporate governance, or investing in it, it's easy to have missed these stakeholder-related developments, but they're important to have on your radar, whether you seek to understand upper management concerns or pursue investment for your business.

The business climate

Outside of broader principles and standards are the aspects of business in which we need to go deep. The focus of this book is climate, as our best-known existential threat. The climate crisis, with the associated poverty it would entail, is, as Paul Polman, former CEO of Unilever, stated, "the biggest intergenerational crime in the history of mankind."[7] We'll discuss the details of the carbon accounting process that forms the baseline of business climate programs later in this book. Beyond that baseline, areas of activity of which you should be aware include:

- Reporting
- Setting GHG reduction targets
- Advocacy

Reporting

The transparency provided by accurate reporting has value on several levels. Reporting commitments help ensure measurement continues to happen internally, generating the intelligence required for strategic action. Genuine and accurate reporting also builds trust with those external to the business, such as direct customers who care about climate impacts, local governments, and stakeholder groups.

CDP, formerly the Carbon Disclosure Project, is known internationally as the platform for reporting climate commitments and progress in reducing GHG emissions. CDP reporting involves answering a detailed questionnaire where you provide answers on governance, climate efforts, and emission quantities, with much of that detail becoming publicly available.

Related voluntary programs to encourage commitments to help ensure better CDP reports in the future include RE100 (committing to purchase 100% renewable energy), EV100 (committing to 100% electric vehicles), and EP100 (improving energy productivity by 100%; the flip side is generating the same amount of revenue with half the energy). Thermodynamics fans might question whether EP100 is even possible, so please note that EP100 requires doubling revenue per unit energy, not necessarily product, and revenue, for better or worse, is not bound in the same way by physical laws. There are certainly opportunities for reduction in the overall energy system, since traditional thermal power (boiler + turbine) is about 35% efficient (35% of input energy is converted to useful electricity), hybrids and EV vehicles from "well to wheel" are 50%–70% more efficient than the internal combustion engine,[8] and LEDs use about one-third to one-fourth the energy[9] of incandescent bulbs that remain in use. However, literally doubling production per unit energy within your facility is quite a lift, and even doubling revenue is a notable challenge.

Target setting

Discussion of voluntary commitments leads us to science-based targets (SBTs).[10] Many years ago, the best understanding of the science popularized that, collectively, countries and companies need to reduce GHG emissions by 80%–90% by 2050. If that's what is needed, then setting targets that are less ambitious than that doesn't make sense. Thus, you set SBTs and reduce emissions at that rate. The logic of SBTs is clear to many businesses, and over 1,500 companies have committed to align to SBTs. Successfully hitting SBTs will provide real progress to highlight in your CDP reports.

SBTs need to be appropriately ambitious in order to be consistent with a scenario of less than 2°C temperature rise (more to come on what that actually means for your business), and achieve results in a 5–15 year timeframe. If you are reading this after July 2022, you need to push for the equivalent of the 1.5°C rise scenario, which is more stringent than achieving less than 2°. The question of whether you set goals that you know you can hit, or you set goals that you need to achieve even if you don't know how to get there, has been an active question for a long time. BHAGs are one dated way to refer to the latter, popularized by management consultant Tom Peters in his encouragement of companies to set "big, hairy, audacious goals!" In the climate realm, I've been all about BHAGs. From one lens, science-based targets actually aren't audacious goals. They represent the targets that we know we need to hit, based on our best understanding of the science, in the same way we know we need delivery systems that actually get our products to customers. Delivering products to within 50 miles of your customers but not actually in their hands isn't helpful. Getting halfway to a science-based target might seem helpful, but you're still short of the goal. If not an audacious goal from the practical sense of needed emissions reduction, however, the amount of retooling, reengineering, and behavioral course correction to hit the targets is an audacious undertaking for very many.

As a promoter of setting SBTs, I've still found it challenging to set them. That is precisely because SBTs should be challenging. It means you're seriously grappling with targets and weighing the boldness of the goal against what you reasonably think you can achieve. Assuming there are repercussions for not hitting the target, you do want to have some level of assurance that you can and will hit the goal.

The real essence of success with SBTs is to know you can make significant headway, trust that you need to be on or better than the less-than-2°-rise path shown in Figure 1.5, and look at SBTs as an

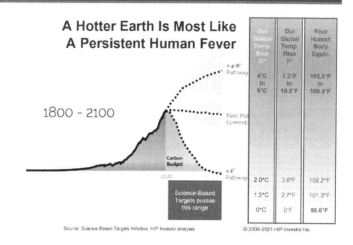

Figure 1.5 Science-Based Targets/HIP Investor.
Source: Science Based Targets Initiative; temperature translations, © HIP (Human Impact + Profit) Investor Inc., www.HIPinvestor.com.

opportunity to learn over 5–15 years of effort. There's much more involved with SBTs than the pass/fail judgment of hitting a goal, and not just any goal, but a goal that the world needs you to set. Through success, you're keeping the global fever down.

As the logical extension of the global business movement toward SBTs, net zero goals reach beyond science-based targets in both scale of emissions and timeframe. The timeframe for achieving net zero goals is often 2040–2050, which is currently beyond the 5–15 years SBT window. The number of businesses with net zero commitments has more than tripled over the course of 2020,[11] with 1,500+ that have stepped up. At least a third of those businesses are in the B Corporation Climate Collective, which is advancing a commitment to net zero by 2030,[12] in recognizing how crucial it is to make GHG emissions reductions well before 2040.

The resources that companies commit to implementing a plan are at least as revealing as the substance of what companies plan to do. The climate-meets-business media network GreenBiz surveys the sustainable business profession biannually, to unearth the trends, drivers, and programs which businesses are advancing. The 2020 survey documents several things, including a continuing shift of CEO attention to sustainability, and increased budgets to put money where mouths are.[13] The survey also casts insights into where sustainability roles typically live within businesses. One finding that tracks my own experience is that supply chain is increasingly involved. Companies increasingly see that their larger climate impacts lie outside their operational boundaries, and once you've doubled down on internal efforts, reaching into the value chain makes complete sense. Companies have less control with suppliers, but work with suppliers holds more potential for impact.

Advocacy

If companies have less control outside their own boundaries, they yet need support and/or third-party actions in those external arenas. Companies weigh in on policy to influence the external. Historically, this hasn't always been helpful on climate fronts, with lobbying dollars driven by fear of government-imposed change hindering climate action. As a result, we now have a great deal of changes to fear, imposed instead by greenhouse gas emissions (Figures 1.6 and 1.7).

Figure 1.6 We Mean Business Logo.
Source: We Mean Business, www.wemeanbusinesscoalition.org.

Figure 1.7 America Is All In Logo.
Source: America Is All In, www.americaisallin.com.

In seeking to help governments adopt sound, proactive, and business-friendly policies, a multiplicity of business coalitions have arisen to promote better climate governance, including the following:

- We Mean Business. An international consortium of seven nonprofits with business membership, We Mean Business highlights businesses active on climate.[14] Over 1,400 companies are involved, including Amazon, American Express, Bank of America, Bloomberg, Campbell's Soup. Conagra, and Chipotle (and that's not even going past letter "C"!).
- America Is All In. In the wake of the U.S. executive branch's withdrawal from the UN Paris Agreement on climate, over 2,200 companies from sole proprietors to multinationals voluntarily stepped up through We Are Still In to affirm to the world that major portions of the United States are committed to the Agreement and dramatic climate action.[15] The coalition pivoted to America Is All In with the return of the United States to the Paris Climate Agreement on January 20, 2021.
- Ceres BICEP. BICEP is a select group of 50+ businesses and investors building business leadership for sustainability, including Autodesk, Aveda, Ben & Jerry's, and Clif Bar (again, invoking the C rule). Over the last 10+ years, Ceres has channeled business voices into public policy, most notably on environmental fronts.[16]
- American Sustainable Business Council. ASBC brings tens of thousands of small businesses into the policy fold, advocating on a range of issues encompassing climate, and generally—if not exclusively—focusing on the federal level.

One area requiring collective advocacy is placing a price on carbon, also known as a carbon tax. ASBC has been active on this issue for years, and the issue was discussed within the Climate Solutions Caucus in the U.S. House of Representatives. The idea is that those generating a ton of GHG emissions should have to pay for doing so, since carbon emissions create so many costly challenges and complications for our economy. Though a price has not been placed on carbon in a meaningful way as of early 2021, it is a development worth monitoring.

In May 2020, the LEAD on Climate coalition, led by Ceres and others, organized what was at the time the largest virtual business advocacy day ever on climate. Cynics might note that if business advocacy and lobbying got us into this mess, particularly those oil-and-gas–dependent sectors that dampened real climate action, why would we endorse more businesses using undue influence to sway our politics? I'd flip that around. If you have businesses out there advocating for what you don't want, why wouldn't you want the rest of us using our influence to push for the right thing?

Zombie carbon

Operational GHG emissions have historically been the focus of GHG tracking and reporting. However, there are additional types of GHG emissions that have neither been tracked well historically nor captured in emission reduction goals.

When you purchase a product, there's an entire supply chain that sourced, manufactured, and delivered that product to you. Embodied carbon refers to the GHG emissions associated with that upstream sourcing, manufacture, and delivery. Those GHGs were emitted before the product ever showed up at your facility, yet linger around like undead waiting to be put to rest, or, in this case, removed from the atmosphere. Zombie carbon is a big issue for the architecture, building engineering, and construction communities, who, in seeking to create highly energy-efficient buildings, run into the fact that many building materials, like concrete and steel, are GHG intensive. A great deal of energy goes into mining and processing metals and minerals. Cement production directly releases great amounts of CO_2. Thus, a new building has a large footprint on day one of its opening, thanks to zombie carbon, even if that footprint is not apparent in looking at the same building's utility bills.

If you are not in architecture, construction, or related industries, but you are a business that has constructed a new building, or plans to do so, zombie carbon is an issue for you. If you compare the energy use of a new building with the old inefficient building that was replaced, your new building will need to save energy over 15–30 years to effectively offset the initial footprint. If it was a greenfield development—a new building that was not a replacement for an old inefficient building—then you simply have the zombie carbon without any comparative savings to credit against. You can make an argument that since it is critical to avoid GHG emissions now, we should defer building until such time in the future when we have more tools to address GHG emissions and potentially more GHG efficient materials. However, that then locks in old inefficient buildings for longer. If left with those two choices, it's not an enviable decision to make.

The real path forward is to use lower embodied carbon materials, so you can build now and minimize climate problems. Cement manufacturers are working with lower GHG production methods. Cross laminated timber (CLT) is composed of large assemblies of engineered wood, and wood is less GHG intensive than concrete or steel. In fact, wood is composed of carbon captured out of the air by trees! CLT can provide the strength needed for larger commercial and institutional buildings, and is seeing increasing interest in the United States as a way to avoid higher impact building materials. (Put a pin in this issue for when we touch on the dangers of deforestation later. Sourcing material for CLT still requires care to avoid the creation of new problems.) Part of the construction solution also lies in reusing buildings to the extent possible, seriously investigating how your inefficient building can become more efficient.

Zombie carbon does not only apply to construction materials. Other purchases where embodied carbon is relevant to your business and your climate strategy are as follows:

- Food. Whether you're a food processor buying the ingredients that are core to your product, or a business where food is a more peripheral input, there is an entire supply chain from farm to fork that generates GHG emissions. That supply chain includes diesel use to sow, grow, and harvest the crop; fertilizers on the farmland; processing energy to get raw crops into more usable form; and distribution of processed food. Different practices within that supply chain have different GHG implications.
- Textiles. Like food, natural fibers like wool, linen, hemp, and cotton come out of farming, with similar supply chains and similar GHG implications. Synthetic fibers are generally made of petroleum and so have very direct GHG impacts.

- Packaging. Packaging types include plastics, paper, cardboard, and metallized film. Most plastics are derived from petroleum and have a footprint similar to synthetic fibers, with processing of petroleum required to create the material. Biobased plastics also have a footprint. Even when sourced from plant material, where carbon was taken out of the air by the plant to generate the material, there are still processing and distribution impacts. Paper similarly has associated GHG emissions.

In the industrial age, and even the information age, it's unavoidable that your purchases have GHG emissions associated with them. It is important to make the effort to quantify and track those emissions. How much are you buying and how GHG intensive is it compared with other purchases?

Up to now, embodied carbon has not been captured well in the processes for quantifying a company's GHG footprint. Organizational footprint tends to focus on operations—the energy and consumables used in the process of conducting business over the course of a year—and not on the embodied carbon of existing infrastructure, physical capital, and product purchases. However, that's changing as companies go more deeply into their supply chain for GHG reductions and think more deeply about climate impacts. In fact, you can no longer ignore the carbon impacts of your purchasing and have a credible climate strategy, unless you can demonstrate those purchases are a relatively insignificant portion of your GHG footprint. To do that, you need to go through the accounting anyway. All purchases on board the GHG accounting ship!

Expect more awareness and innovation around reducing embodied carbon. Expect more requirements for businesses to track and report embodied carbon—at least non-regulatory requirements that are associated with voluntary reporting programs—in the years to come.

Cross-cutting issues

Though climate is our focus, it behooves us to understand other issues that we need to tackle in the sustainable business quest, both to understand competing priorities and to look for synergies.

Die, packaging, die

Plastics pollution has been a known issue for decades, yet without serious uptake or consideration by mainstream media. With that as the baseline, I am honestly shocked at how much life the issue has taken on in the past few years. The proliferation of video has certainly helped inject new life into pollution awareness. You can talk about sea turtles being impaled by straws, but until you and a million of your colleagues watch it in painful detail, you don't have the visceral reaction.

So much of that plastic is packaging. And packaging provides a real service in protecting product. If it didn't, we wouldn't use so much of it in the first place. The challenge is this: how do you provide strong product packaging that's resilient to breakdown, yet once product is delivered, it becomes easy to break down? Styrofoam— or expanded polystyrene, more generically—is wonderfully light and rigid. Once it's served its purpose, those qualities that were so helpful become impressively unhelpful if you want to concentrate it for better recycling or reclaim it for reuse. Part of the solution lies in design. For example, using plastic film airbags that only use a small fraction of the plastic previously used to protect product.

Ideally, you have living packaging that maintains itself while protecting product, and then "dies" once it has served its purpose. Nature has that solution. It's called a citrus peel. Also, walnut shells, coconut husks, and a wide range of other packaging that protects seeds and then biodegrades after their purpose has been served. We've seen alternatives pushing in that direction: corn-based packing peanuts that dissolve in water, and mushroom- and mycelium-based alternatives to styrofoam. Those alternatives address padding, but less so the films directly around product. The shelf-life challenge persists, where films need to last at least as long as product stays on the shelf. Sustainable Packaging Coalition, The Sustainability Consortium, and OSC2 (One Step Closer) are all business associations that have tackled and are tackling the problem. *Forbes Magazine* documents individual efforts by companies like BASF, Verizon, and HP.[17] Ellen Macarthur Foundation is ushering in the new plastics economy,[18] where plastics don't become pollution. Their three principles:

- Eliminate all problematic and unnecessary plastic items
- Innovate to ensure that the plastics we do need are reusable, recyclable, or compostable

- Circulate all the plastic items we use to keep them in the economy and out of the environment

With the proliferation of the circular economy, companies increasingly see their products as assets that they own. They then have responsibility for those products even when being used by far-flung customers, and have incentive to reclaim them. This concept can be extended to the packaging, with companies providing packaging as a service (so PaaS?).

Plastics are overwhelmingly produced from the same source that drives a vast amount of our GHG emissions troubles—fossil fuel. Biodegradable plastics are generally biobased and not produced from fossil fuel. Biobased plastics are also typically less GHG intensive than their petroleum counterparts, as reported in the journal *Nature* in 2019[19] as well as in multiple other studies that I've seen.

Note you have to be careful with biodegradable versus compostable as terms. The former could mean the plastic simply breaks down into much smaller pieces of plastic that are problematic in living systems. Compostable, as certified by the Biodegradable Products Institute, means the plastic can be fully broken down.

Reusable, recyclable, and compostable plastics will need to make inroads to reduce the plastic pollution problem. As it stands, we're left for now with immense amounts of plastic in natural environments, particularly oceans. A select group of companies are sourcing ocean plastics to incorporate into their own products, which is a strong story for a business that needs plastics and wants to demonstrate responsible production practices. Ultimately, the magnitude of that solution is not a match to the magnitude of the problem. All can agree our oceans should not serve as temporary plastic reservoirs to correct for bad disposal practices. Oceans must instead serve as the hosts of thriving marine life, as they have in the past, and as they will hopefully continue to do for eons to come.

Back on the ranch

In addition to packaging and the associated plastic pollution that has become a heightened concern for businesses, another evolution that affects both climate and business is the extension of organic to beyond-organic farming, fiber, and foods. Even if you're not directly working in food processing or textiles, you source food for events, have investments relating to agriculture, and/or have other farm touchpoints. Regenerative agriculture is now a popular term, where the key concept involves farming as a tool to maintain and even improve the health of the soil. For the climate, a key portion of that is building soil carbon by using crops to capture carbon out of the air. Agriculture becomes a process to remove CO_2 from the air, complementing your efforts to reduce your CO_2 emissions into the air.

That key concept leads to some key questions: How do you know you're doing it? How do you gauge to what extent you are regenerative? Making regenerative claims, but without a definition or other parameters against which you can measure whether or not you are "regenerative" is risky at best. To address that risk, The Carbon Underground, representing a network of food and fiber businesses, offers a definition.[20]

> Practices that (i) contribute to generating/building soils and soil fertility and health; (ii) increase water percolation, water retention, and clean and safe water run off; (iii) increase biodiversity and ecosystem health and resiliency; and (iv) invert the carbon emissions of our current agriculture to one of remarkably significant carbon sequestration thereby cleansing the atmosphere of legacy levels of CO_2.

Included practices are several: no-till/minimum tillage, use of cover crops and crop rotations, inoculation of soils with composts or compost extracts, and well-managed grazing practices.

The established organic standard for foods has clear guidelines that already support some regenerative practices. Several regenerative agriculture standards are under development to better capture and codify those practices:

- Soil Carbon Index. With the stated goal to build "soil health and increasing soil carbon sequestration,"[21] SCI takes an outcome-based approach. Rather than dictate practices, SCI asks farmers to measure results in four areas: soil organic carbon, water infiltration/holding capacity, "aggregate stability" (clumping of soil), and microbes in the soil.

- Regenerative Organic Certification. Rodale Institute, leader in organic for decades, launched a regenerative organic certification standard[22] in partnership with the Regenerative Organic Alliance that has both required practices and optional practices[23] built around the three pillars shown in Figure 1.8—Soil Health, Animal Welfare, Social Fairness. Those involved seek to go beyond simple soil regeneration to social regeneration, including the relationships we have with the range of lifeforms that provide our food.
- Ecological Outcome Verification (Land to Market). The Savory Institute maintains a laser focus on the role of grazing animals to regenerate landscapes, capturing the Carbon Underground's sense of "well-managed grazing." Similar to SCI, EOV takes an outcome-based approach, measuring key indicators of soil health, biodiversity, and ecosystem function shown in Figure 1.9.

SOIL HEALTH   ANIMAL WELFARE   SOCIAL FAIRNESS

Figure 1.8 ROA.
Source: Regenerative Organic Alliance.

Figure 1.9 EOV.
Source: Savory Institute.

These standards take a more holistic approach than focusing solely on climate and carbon benefits, incorporating biodiversity, animal welfare, and social fairness. The development of these standards is recent, and the full extent of market uptake remains to be seen. The price point for products developed under these standards is expected to be higher than market, because they're creating higher value—in healthy soils, landscape dynamics, and quality of life for life. Higher price points hold potential to make more money for farmers. Whether they generate better margins will depend on the costs involved.

Taking carbon out of the air and sequestering it in soil (sequestering back into soil, where carbon was lost) is a huge opportunity. One point of contention for the field (both the field of practice and the literal farm field) is how long term the carbon is stored. Do the increases we measure in the soil at the end of the growing season stay locked in for decades, or is it ephemeral, re-released into the air through microbial or other action? More on that later.

Another tactic for the climate-friendly livestock ranch is not going there at all. The rise of plant-based meats holds the promise of high-quality, low-carbon-emissions protein. Plant-based eating has been around for decades, and generally known to have lower GHG impact when comparing legumes with conventional meat. What's changed is how closely plant-based foods now simulate meat, in theory appealing to a broader audience. Impossible Foods released a study that indicates their Impossible Burger has 10% the GHG footprint, water consumption, and water degradation of beef.[24] A study conducted for Beyond Meat, another plant-based meat provider, shows a very similar GHG footprint result, with even lower water footprint.[25] The health concerns that whole food advocates have around highly processed food still apply to these plant-based meats, and concerns are heightened for products cultured in laboratories rather than on landscapes. Given the investment in plant-based, as well as acceptance from hamburger fans, plant-based is going to be around for a while as the next iteration of meat alternatives, even for those ignoring the compelling environmental stats.

Whiskey's for drinking

Both plant-based meat studies looked at water as an impact metric as well as GHG emissions. Water is critical for agriculture. Water is not only a critical input for our businesses and supply chains, but it is also intertwined with climate and climate-related issues.

Energy use is the root cause of a vast portion of our carbon footprint. Energy is needed to power our buildings and businesses, grow food, create clothing, and provide packaging. There are situations where water and energy can substitute for each other, like a choice of cleaning process where one option is energy-intensive and the other is water-intensive. If only governed by a climate goal, you would be tempted to avoid energy use and choose the water-intensive process. And if you live in a water-scarce area, water-intensive processing would be a poor choice. Complicating the situation, the climate crisis has direct impacts on water availability that are crucial to take into account. The net effect of using more GHG-intensive energy could in the collective also drive water shortage. In order to avoid the tradeoffs that come from putting on your climate blinders too narrowly, it's important to have an awareness of water issues and how water relates to your business.

Reduced availability of water tends to lead to reduced goodwill. "Whiskey's for drinking, water's for fighting over" is an-often-attributed-if-unverified quote of Mark Twain. Whether or not Mr. Twain observed conflicts over water over a century ago, another negative impact of the climate crisis almost certainly invites those conflicts—wide swings in water availability. If the Hopi give us koyaanisqatsi, the Lakota of the upper Great Plains give us mni wiconi. Water is life. Life is worth fighting for. And where you need water for your supply chain and operations to function, you'll be fighting, too.

As critical as fresh water is, what's impressive to me is the extent to which it's undervalued. For eons, it has (1) been relatively plentiful throughout much of the world, (2) fallen from the sky without any effort on our behalf, and (3) gravity-delivered to us where water in the form of snow lands at high altitude and flows down to nearby flatlands, whether intentionally through aquifers or more commonly in the form of the rivers on which so much of humanity depends.

By undervalued, I'm not strictly talking about the economics. Though those who can pay more should be willing to pay more for water, from another lens, water has to be a human right, and a right for all life. You can find lifeforms that get by on impressively small amounts of water, but all life requires it. Value to me is better expressed in how willing we are to waste it, whether we're paying $0.001 per gallon from the local utility, or $10 per gallon equivalent for the gold-plated version of your favorite bottled water. And wasting, we are. The EPA estimates that 10% of homes leak 90 or more gallons per day, with the average home wasting 10,000 gallons per year.[26] If correct, that's over 1 trillion gallons of water wasted in the United States that could be used to meet water demand in businesses and homes. Compare that with the World Health Organization baseline water need of 6 gallons per person per day (gppd).[27] Water is clearly too easy to waste. I have much respect for the people—mostly women and children—who walk on the order of miles every day to carry as much water as they can for their families and lives. They know the value of water and don't take it for granted. The UN documents that 700 million to 4 billion people are subject to water scarcity.[28]

Wasting water is different from wasting non-renewable resources, as water generally cycles between different reservoirs. A portion of fresh water waste flows downstream to support aquatic life. Given the effort to purify and deliver water to our businesses, it's right to be vigilant to eliminate that waste. However, it doesn't mean that wasted water is completely lost. It likely finds its way back to groundwater or provides fresh inflow to a local waterway. Our mission with water, as I think about it, is to (1) maintain our fresh water reservoirs; (2) slow the rate at which fresh is converted to saltwater (with fresh finding its way to sea by a range of pathways); and (3) staying within the carrying capacity of the water bodies that support us, without withdrawing water from reservoirs faster than it is recharged.

Judith Schwartz, author of *Water in Plain Sight*, concludes 10% of the world's food comes from taking more from groundwater than is recharged.[29] Concerns on the long-term viability of fresh water resources, driven by similar insights, have helped launch efforts like the Water Footprint Network. Their interrogation of the issue has led to a multiplicity of water definitions, including:[30]

• blue water (sourced from groundwater or other water bodies),
• green water (stored in the root zone of soil and very important for agriculture and ecosystems), and
• gray water (the water needed to dilute pollutants to meet discharge standards).

I find this differentiation helpful, as it promotes the understanding that you don't need potable fresh water for all uses. It is typically blue water we most need to conserve. Near-surface soils become a reservoir of green water courtesy of precipitation, and proper management of soils allows them to store water and reduce demand on blue water. According to Malin Falkenmark of the Stockholm International Water Institute, two-thirds of precipitation becomes green water,[31] so there's much green water with which to work.

For the private sector, evaluating watersheds and the corporate role in ensuring carrying capacity is an emerging practice. General Mills staff have evaluated the watersheds from which they source ingredients, supporting water stewardship plan development across the globe for the most material and at-risk watersheds.[32] See Figure 1.10.

The risk elements are clear for any business whose suppliers are remotely connected to a healthy water cycle. Valuing water, becoming keenly aware of the potential disruptions to your supply chain, and creating redundancies and back-up plans with at-risk suppliers will be a significant part of the game moving forward. It's important to develop water resilience plans along with climate strategy, so water disruptions don't disrupt your climate plans and more.

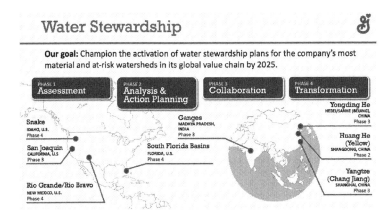

Figure 1.10 Water Stewardship—GM.
Source: General Mills. Used with permission of General Mills.

The International Living Future Institute has helped introduce the concept of "net positive water," where a building's water needs are met through precipitation and/or onsite recycled water, taking the concept of operating within your local watershed capacity and bringing it down to site boundaries.[33] With net positive, you are producing as much clean water as you are consuming onsite. Challenging, but exactly the right goal, considering the health of the water cycle and the current extent to which we overdraw on water sources.

Whether we're looking at climate-friendly agriculture, climate-friendly materials to reduce embodied carbon, or better water management in conjunction with climate action, it's important to be able to fully participate in real climate solutions. The more people that embrace climate solutions, the better off we will be as companies and communities. That requires tackling the barriers that prevent people from doing so.

JEDI master

If decades in the making, there is now broad recognition that diversity and inclusion among and within our staff and suppliers are required as part of the broader sustainability portfolio. To start, there is a diversity of program acronyms—DI, DEI, EDI, JEDI—depending on whether you choose to emphasize justice, equity, diversity, and/or inclusion, looking at race, gender, age, sexual orientation, physical ability, language ability, or other distinguishing aspects of a person. Unless you were in a sector that was already under diversity scrutiny, like tech, you could have gotten away without a program even just a few years ago. But not now. 2017 was the year of the Inclusion Challenge among the B Corporation community.[34] Those of us rooted in things environment may have a hard time seeing our role in inclusion efforts that look like an HR function, but all have a role to play in ensuring workplaces are supportive and welcoming to the broadest possible spectrum of people.

The thrust of DEI programs is to ensure that underrepresented groups (those who've historically been disadvantaged) are given opportunities, with race, gender, ability, and sexual orientation comprising key categories of underrepresentation. Lack of representation can have multiple drivers. A common root of underrepresentation and lack of diversity is discrimination, based on not only the differences those with hiring power perceive, but also the chain of education and other events that need to happen for someone of any background to become a skilled and eligible employee. For centuries, discrimination based on gender, skin color, geographic origin, orientation, and religion has disadvantaged many peoples. Fear of change within an established community can inspire discrimination, tied to fear of the "other" coming into that community.

We're working in real time to reverse this historic fact, and build on the decades of progress that has been made. It is crucial for business success. We see the power of diversity in business through the range of skill sets a business needs to be successful: marketing, accounting, design/engineering, project execution, and leadership. Marketing itself is best informed by a range of staff that reflect the range of possible customers and possible customer perspectives, allowing for the greatest market intelligence. Applying a broad range of perspectives is often the most effective approach to problem-solving in general. Business is only able to realize the power of that diversity if it cultivates a workplace that is welcoming to the broadest spectrum of people.

Self-interest in business success notwithstanding, the call to be just is also being heard. The response of the business community to the George Floyd racial injustice protests was unprecedented, with many organizations that had never before issued a statement on race suddenly affirming in 2020 that Black Lives do indeed Matter. How you conduct your business to avoid the circumstances that ignite racial injustice protests is another matter, involving investment and an entire process taking you well beyond simply making a statement. Those genuinely oriented to the problem will tackle where and how discrimination shows up in the company.

People with different appearances, customs, languages, and beliefs have often been seen as threats by those already established in a given place. That sense of threat might not even be in our awareness, but it has filtered and will filter into the decisions of business owners, in hiring, contracting, and more. What's clear in that shaping of decisions is that the benefits of diversity are held back. And thus, the need for DEI programs to help all companies become JEDI masters, advance social justice, and capture the value of diversity.

We've now reviewed a host of trends that relate to climate:

- Sustainable Development Goals vision and comprehensive standards for business that include climate and more
- Business-led climate-related activities including reporting, target-setting, and advocacy
- Embodied carbon as the carbon footprint of your purchases before they reach your facility
- Additional trends around the key purchases of packaging, food, textiles, and water
- Diversity and equity efforts that will help all fully engage in climate and affirm a belief in justice

It's important to understand the trends in order to understand the potential for competing priorities, assuming your company has limited resources to invest the bucket it considers sustainability issues (even if those issues don't live in isolation from your procurement, marketing, and operations). At least as important a reason to understand the landscape is to identify the synergies where climate efforts can support and address other issues.

Now let's move to the core of our work together: the specifics of crafting bold climate strategy.

Notes

1 Jeffrey Sachs et al., "Sustainable Development Report 2020", Sustainable Development Report, June 30, 2020. https://sdgindex.org/reports/sustainable-development-report-2020/
2 "Business Roundtable Redefines the Purpose of a Corporation to Promote 'An Economy That Serves All Americans'", Business Roundtable, August 19, 2019. https://www.businessroundtable.org/business-roundtable-redefines-the-purpose-of-a-corporation-to-promote-an-economy-that-serves-all-americans
3 Laurel Wamsley, "World's Largest Asset Manager Puts Climate at the Center of Its Investment Strategy", National Public Radio, January 14, 2020. https://www.npr.org/2020/01/14/796252481/

worlds-largest-asset-manager-puts-climate-at-the-center-of-its-investment-strate

4 Larry Fink, "Larry Fink's 2021 Letter to CEOs", Blackrock, January 2021. https://www.blackrock.com/corporate/investor-relations/larry-fink-ceo-letter

5 #BlackRocksBigProblem, 2021. https://www.blackrocksbigproblem.com/

6 Clara Ferreira Marques, "Stocks Rout Poses a $30 Trillion Ethical Test", Bloomberg News, March 12, 2020. https://www.bloomberg.com/opinion/articles/2020-03-12/esg-investing-faces-30-trillion-test-with-market-rout

7 Sarah Butler, "Ex-Unilever Boss Seeks 'Heroic CEOs' to Tackle Climate Change and Inequality", The Guardian, July 21, 2019. https://www.theguardian.com/business/2019/jul/21/ex-unilever-boss-seeks-heroic-ceos-to-tackle-climate-change-and-inequality-paul-polman

8 Alternative Fuels Data Center, "Emissions from Hybrid and Plug-In Electric Vehicles", U.S. Department of Energy, 2021. https://afdc.energy.gov/vehicles/electric_emissions.html

9 Office of Energy Efficiency & Renewable Energy, "How Energy-Efficient Light Bulbs Compare with Traditional Incandescents", U.S. Department of Energy, 2021. https://www.energy.gov/energysaver/save-electricity-and-fuel/lighting-choices-save-you-money/how-energy-efficient-light

10 "Science Based Targets: Driving Ambitious Corporate Climate Action", Science Based Targets Initiative, 2021. http://www.sciencebasedtargets.org

11 James Murray and Tom Gockelen-Koslowski, "Global Net-Zero Commitments Double in Less than a Year", GreenBiz Group, September 23, 2020. https://www.greenbiz.com/article/global-net-zero-commitments-double-less-year

12 Net Zero 2030, B Corp Climate Collective, 2021. https://www.bcorpclimatecollective.org/net-zero-2030

13 John Davies et al., State of the Profession 2020 Report, GreenBiz Group, January 2020. https://www.greenbiz.com/report/state-profession-2020-report

14 We Mean Business, "About Us", We Mean Business Coalition, 2021. https://www.wemeanbusinesscoalition.org/about/

15 We Are Still In, "Success Stories", We Are Still In, 2020. https://www.wearestillin.com/success

16 Ceres, "Ceres Policy Network", Ceres, 2021. https://www.ceres.org/networks/ceres-policy-network

17 Kevin O'Marah, "Circular Economy Is the Answer", Forbes, October 26, 2017. https://www.forbes.com/sites/kevinomarah/2017/10/26/circular-economy-is-the-answer/#5053bd693e2e

18 Ellen MacArthur Foundation, "New Plastics Economy", Ellen MacArthur Foundation, 2017. https://www.newplasticseconomy. org/

19 Jiajia Zheng and Sangwon Suh, "Strategies to Reduce the Global Carbon Footprint of Plastics", *Nature Climate Change*, **9**, 374–378 (2019). https://www.nature.com/articles/s41558-019-0459-z

20 The Carbon Underground, "Definition", The Carbon Underground, 2021. https://thecarbonunderground.org/our-initiative/definition/

21 Soil Carbon Initiative, "Executive Summary", Soil Carbon Initiative, 2019. https://www.soilcarboninitiative.org/executive-summary

22 Rodale Institute, "Regenerative Organic Agriculture", Rodale Institute, 2021. https://rodaleinstitute.org/why-organic/organic-basics/regenerative-organic-agriculture/

23 Regenerative Organic Alliance, "Regenerative Organic Certification", Regenerative Organic Alliance, 2021. https://regenorganic. org/

24 Sofia Khan et al., "Environmental Life Cycle Analysis: Impossible Burger 2.0", Impossible Foods, 2020. https://impossiblefoods.com/mission/lca-update-2019/

25 Martin Heller et al., "Beyond Meat's Beyond Burger Life Cycle Assessment, University of Michigan Center for Sustainable Systems", 2018. http://css.umich.edu/publication/beyond-meats-beyond-burger-life-cyclē-assessment-detailed-comparison-between-plant-based

26 U.S. EPA, "Fix A Leak Week", U.S. EPA, 2020. https://www.epa.gov/watersense/fix-leak-week

27 Brian Reed and Bob Reed, "How Much Water Is Needed in Emergencies?", World Health Organization, 2013. https://www.who.int/water_sanitation_health/emergencies/WHO_TN_09_How_much_water_is_needed.pdf

28 United Nations, Water Scarcity, United Nations, 2020. https://www.unwater.org/water-facts/scarcity/

29 Excerpted from Judith Schwartz, *Water in Plain Sight*. "Ten Facts about the Water We Use", Chelsea Green, 2019. https://www.chelseagreen.com/2019/ten-facts-about-the-water-we-waste/

30 Water Footprint Network, "What Is a Water Footprint?", Water FootprintNetwork,2019.https://waterfootprint.org/en/water-footprint/what-is-water-footprint/

31 Excerpted from Judith Schwartz, *Water in Plain Sight*. "Ten Facts about the Water We Use", Chelsea Green, 2019. https://www.chelseagreen.com/2019/ten-facts-about-the-water-we-waste/

32 Presentation by Jeff Hanratty of General Mills, Sustainable Food Trade Association webinar, General Mills, April 2020.

33 Living Building Challenge, "Water Petal Intent", International Living Future Institute, 2017. https://living-future.org/lbc-3_1/water-petal/
34 B Corporation, "Inclusive Economy Challenge", B Lab, 2017. https://bcorporation.net/for-b-corps/inclusive-economy-challenge

Chapter 2

Block and tackle your climate strategy

> In many spheres of human endeavor, from science to business to education to economic policy, good decisions depend on good measurement.
> – Ben Bernanke, former Chair of the Federal Reserve

For you to be successful on climate fronts, you will need to:

- Craft bold climate strategy
- Implement the strategy, applying tips, tools, and best practices
- Avoid pitfalls by learning from the lessons of others

In order to craft your strategy, we'll work through the key steps to quantify your baseline climate impact, set bold climate targets, and measure progress toward those targets.

In the process of quantifying a business's greenhouse gas footprint (often also called carbon footprint or GHG inventory), your mission, should you choose to accept it, is to:

- Set boundaries
- Collect data
- Apply emission factors
- Conduct quality control
- Report results

The footprint forms the core of your climate strategy, allowing you to see exactly what it is that you need to reduce. The five steps are

DOI: 10.4324/9781003191544-3

a paraphrase of the GHG Protocol, the international standard of over 15 years that guides how we come up with carbon footprint numbers,[1] and which provides the backbone of GHG accounting.

Set boundaries and collect data

To determine the boundaries within which you will account for emissions, there are two basic approaches for organizations:

- Operational control. The facilities, fleets, and other equipment that you own and operate are within your GHG boundary.
- Financial control. The assets over which you have financial control are within the boundary, even if you don't operate them.

These approaches seek to identify where you are making decisions that generate GHG emissions. Most companies that are creating products and operating physical assets use operational control. Even services companies that are managing offices for staff providing services use operational control. Financial control is suited primarily to holding companies and investment firms that control the purse strings over assets and whose decisions over those assets have GHG implications. The majority of you reading this will be using operational control.

Within those boundaries, then, the basic task is to quantify seven types of GHGs, as established by the GHG Protocol and shown in Figure 2.1.

For most organizations, carbon dioxide (CO_2) is overwhelmingly the largest portion of their organizational footprint. Methane (CH_4), nitrous oxide (N_2O), and hydrofluorocarbons (HFCs) play smaller roles, and the remaining three GHGs are only of concern in select industrial processes.

Emissions of these GHGs are categorized as either Scope 1, Scope 2, or Scope 3.

- Scope 1 emissions are the emissions coming directly out of the things you own and operate: combustion of fuels in your facilities and vehicle fleet, escape of refrigerants and other gases.

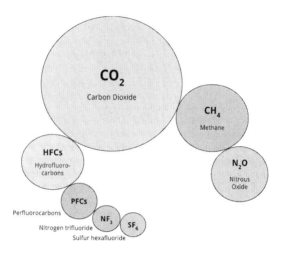

Figure 2.1 GHG Bubbles.
Source: Author, inspiration from the Climate Fund of Sri Lanka.

- Scope 2 emissions are the emissions tied to your activities, but which happen off-site (indirect). Electricity emissions are the primary Scope 2 emissions, as even though you are making on-site choices that increase or decrease electricity use, the emissions generated are at the power plant at the other end of the wires. If you purchase heat or steam for your operations that generates off-site GHG, like through a district heating system, emissions from that energy are also Scope 2.
- Scope 3. Everything else. Scope 3 emissions are the emissions that happen throughout your value chain as a cost of doing business. Scope 3 includes Tier 1/2/3 suppliers, packaging, product freight, customer product use, and more. It also includes activities that are peripheral to product flow, like business travel and employee commute.

Apply emission factors

The complication in quantifying emissions is that you don't have information on direct emissions of CO_2, CH_4, and other gases.

What you do have is information on the sources that generate GHGs. To calculate GHG emissions, take the data you have on sources—gallons, therms, kWh, passenger-miles, etc.—and apply the secret sauce of emission factors that translates those numbers into amounts of gases. The GHG Protocol provides a set of emission factors, though you will generally need to supplement from other sources. The U.S. EPA provides a convenient set of GHG emission factors for U.S. businesses. Other potential sources include the U.K.'s DEFRA, The Climate Registry, and the Intergovernmental Panel on Climate Change.

In addition to the emissions of each gas, you also want to know the relative impact of that gas. Different gases have different global warming potentials. A ton of one gas might contribute more or less to global warming than a ton of other gases. In the interests of having just one measure, global warming potentials (GWPs) are applied to each gas to translate everything into units of metric tons of carbon dioxide equivalent ($MTCO_2E$). Because CO_2 is typically such a large portion of the contribution, it is the measure by which other gases are evaluated. You can generally find GWPs in the emission factor sources listed above, though the ultimate source is the Intergovernmental Panel on Climate Change, which issues climate assessment reports roughly every six years.[2]

Some gases last longer than others in the atmosphere. Most prominently, methane breaks down (technically, it oxidizes) over time. Among the GWP parlor tricks that you can theoretically play is to adjust the timeframe over which you're looking. In theory, if you extend the timeframe further into the future, the amount of remaining methane drops as it oxidizes, and methane is then less of an issue. However, international reporting standards usually require use of 100-year GWP, aligned with understanding long-term climate impacts, so parlor tricks aren't really an option. The drawback of this approach is that it ignores the higher amounts of methane that are present in earlier years. Use of a 20-year timeframe would more strongly encourage you to look at methane reduction, and companies that have significant methane in their supply chain (beef operations, natural gas distribution, wastewater plants, rice farming, etc.) would be wise to track down shorter-term GWPs and further investigate.

To summarize our greenhouse gas footprint path:

- Gather the usage amounts of each emissions source (kWh, gallons, therms, etc.)
- Apply the emission factor (kg gas per kWh, gallon, therm, etc.) for each GHG
- Apply the GWP of each GHG to get kg (and then metric tons) of CO_2 equivalent emissions

In the remote chance you want a formula to capture those steps, try the below.

$$\sum \text{Purchased Amount}_n \times \text{Emission Factor}_{n,\text{GHG}} \times \text{GWP}_{\text{GHG}} = \text{GHG Baseline (MTCO}_2\text{E)}.$$

Since you have the gallons, therms, and kWh that come from your operations for Scope 1 and Scope 2 data, following this approach will generate your baseline numbers. Conduct quality control to make sure you got it right, and you're set for reporting your Scope 1 and Scope 2 baselines!

In terms of level of effort, there are two primary factors that come to play: (1) whether data are already in electronic format and (2) the number of data points. I generally find calculating the footprint of natural gas and electricity to be straightforward. A great number of you can download data directly from your utility, and where the number of meters is relatively manageable, the process is manageable (though if you have dozens of facilities with submetering, it can add up). Areas where more effort is generally needed include the following:

- Refrigerants. HFCs are the GHG of concern, and those are in HVAC units as well as refrigerators. If all your units are serviced, the service provider can tell you how much was recharged, and that's straightforward. If not serviced, there is a process through which to calculate the default HFC loss, and that can get involved when you have dozens or hundreds of HVAC units.

- Vehicle fleet. Even in the 2020s, data aren't always in electronic and you may need to work with fuel logs. Over the course of a year, even a small fleet of vehicles might generate hundreds of data points to aggregate.

Bang head against Scope 3

Scope 3 is a different animal than Scopes 1 and 2. To quantify your footprint, a major issue with Scope 3 is that you have less data and less control over your supply chain, compared with Scopes 1 and 2 of your operations. It's also a very diverse scope with a range of data needs. Categories of those Scope 3 emissions include the following:[3]

1. Purchased goods and services. The consumable supplies that are purchased by your business have an upstream impact driven by the energy and other resources required to produce them (that is, zombie carbon). This category is routinely one of the largest and most prominent GHG contributors for businesses that create a product.
2. Capital goods. Similar to Category 1, this category is used for the equipment and other longer-term purchases made by your company. Along with Category 1, Category 2 is where zombie carbon comes into organizational accounting, as the capital goods footprint represents what went into creating that equipment.
3. Fuel- and energy-related activities (not included in Scope 1 or 2). Scopes 1 and 2 generally address oil and gas combustion and operational electricity use. This category captures processing of energy sources to get them into a usable form as well as transmission and distribution losses in getting energy to your plant or office.
4. Upstream transportation and distribution. Whether your supplies get to you by truck, rail, sea, or air, there are emissions associated with their delivery.
5. Waste generated in operations. Solid waste, recycling, and compost material streams have associated climate-impacting emissions (and you're generally going to be incentivized to recycle and compost in seeking GHG reductions).

6. Business travel. I'm calling this category self-explanatory.
7. Employee commuting. See Category 6.
8. Upstream leased assets. If your business leases equipment or buildings, and those emissions are not already captured in Scopes 1 and 2, the associated emissions should be accounted for here.
9. Downstream transportation and distribution. This involves the distribution system after your product leaves the gates of your company, extending to your immediate customer and potentially to the ultimate end user, if that is not your direct customer.
10. Processing of sold products. See Category 11. Category 10 is simply an intermediate step to use of sold products, and if not processed by the product user, those emissions should be captured by reporting.
11. Use of sold products. For those that make clothes that need to be washed, food that needs to be cooked, or equipment that needs to be powered, that product use footprint is also part of your value chain.
12. End-of-life treatment of sold products. Ultimate product disposal can also generate GHGs, often in landfill, though recycling and composting also contribute emissions.
13. Downstream leased assets. As the flip side of Category 8, if your business leases assets to others, account for those impacts here. These could be products that you own and rent to others, if those were not already captured in Category 11.
14. Franchises. Companies that use a franchise model should be capturing the impacts of their franchisees.
15. Investments. This category is primarily relevant to financial services companies. The stocks, bonds, and other investments your company may hold are not generally included here.

Credit goes to the GHG Protocol for articulating those categories. All Scope 3 categories are shown graphically in Figure 2.2, along with Scopes 1 and 2.

We now have seven GHGs, three Scopes, and 15 categories of Scope 3. I'm about to add four approaches. Hang in there!

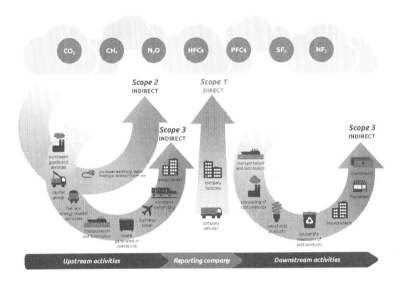

Figure 2.2 GHG Scopes.
Source: WRI/WBCSD Greenhouse Gas Protocol Scope 3 Standard (2011, revised 2013).

In tackling Scope 3, it is critical to think through:

• how you're quantifying the Scope 3 baseline that will be the basis by which you'll measure reductions over time, and
• how readily you'll be able to track progress toward targets.

The process for categories like upstream transportation, waste, and business travel is relatively well-defined and similar to Scopes 1 and 2: tally fuel use, ton-miles, or whatever is the relevant measure, apply emission factors, and apply global warming potentials. The category that is particularly complex is purchased goods and services—Category 1 of those Scope 3 emissions. Teams that have grappled with addressing greenhouse gas emissions know that companies can take a range of approaches to quantify the Purchased

Goods and Services baseline, and those approaches include the following:

A. Estimates based on purchasing dollars. For every dollar you purchase of printer paper, cleaning chemicals, coffee, or any other purchase, there is some amount of GHG that is generated. The assumption in this approach is that amount per dollar can be accurately calculated. Find the right database that can tell you exactly what that amount is, and you can use your purchasing records to come up with a supply chain footprint. The EIO-LCA database that used to serve as a resource on this front is now dated. USEEIO from the U.S. EPA[4] and Exiobase are alternatives with more recent data, but less user-friendly and best accessed through life cycle assessment (LCA) experts.
B. Estimates based on purchasing weights. Rather than associate each purchasing dollar with some amount of GHG, each pound of office supplies, ingredients, and other purchases are associated with some amount of GHG. LCA is the tool to generate GHG estimates from weights of purchased goods. LCA tools to calculate that GHG can be quite complex, and effectively allow you to model the creation of a given purchase. Emission results depend on supplier production process and more.
C. Collecting actual data on the company's supply chain. Rather than employ estimation tools, here you work with your supplier to get data on building energy, transport fuel, and other GHG sources used to create the products that you buy.
D. A hybrid of the above three approaches, given different data availability for different purchases.

Companies often go with approach A or B. In many cases, it's hard to get the actual data for approach C, even if the emerging guidance is pushing companies toward this approach. For example, if you're a cereal company sourcing rice flour, it's difficult to actually measure rice paddy methane (growing rice generates methane) over the growing season. A and B approaches are fine, if built around an accurate source, for generating a baseline emissions number you can report for your Scope 3 emissions. I generally use approach B. Enter the purchasing dollars or pounds by supply, and you'll get an impact number. However, know those pathways are problematic if you want to measure improvements against that baseline number.

To illustrate, consider the following: you go with approach A, using purchasing dollars, and you access a database that ties those dollars to a GHG/$ metric (that is, the database knows that a dollar's worth of paper has X kg of emissions and a dollar's worth of plastic film generates Y kg). You don't need a Ph.D. in math (but if you do have one, super-cool!) to see that there are only three ways to demonstrate GHG reduction:

- You buy less (so the purchasing dollars go down).
  - Unless you're trying to downscale your business, purchasing less isn't an option, outside of some efficiency improvements, which will play out after you've optimized processes and eliminated waste.
- Industry-wide shifts change the GHG/$ metric in the database (so GHG/$ goes down).
  - Making the GHG/$ metric go down goes well beyond the actions of one company. Shifts in that metric are unlikely to happen within a three-year goal timeline and may not even happen in 5–10 years (unless, of course, all supplier industries are tackling emissions like we know they should). There are also time lags involved: the time required for a study to be done (academic studies are often a data source), and the subsequent time to update the database after new numbers come in.
- The company sources something different, if that's an option (substituting a purchase with lower GHG/$).

The only business-savvy action that you can take to reduce your GHG emissions is the third substitution option. If you can't do that, you're stuck with your baseline emissions until you purchase less or the entire supplier industry starts emitting less.

Your company will run into the same issue if using approach B rather than approach A. Rather than GHG/$, you're working with GHG/lb or GHG/kg, but you're still left with the analogous three GHG reduction options.

However, even if your calculation options above are limited, there is an action specific to your circumstance that you can take: work with your suppliers on improvements. *What should happen under any of the approaches is that you identify emission reduction priorities for your supply chain to implement: use more efficient equipment, install renewable energy, improve management practices, shift fuels, avoid wastage, etc.* Rather than the substitution option, you can keep the same supplier relationships and help those suppliers become that much better. In working with your suppliers, measure their improvement and then have real progress data—kWh of solar generated, kWh of utility energy reduced, etc.—to compare with your Purchased Goods and Services baseline.

Thus, there is value in using purchasing dollars and LCA results for Scope 3 estimates:

- Can they help you prioritize where to focus? Absolutely.
- Can you use that to target improvements in your supply chain (such as investing in renewables with key partners) and to quantify that improvement? Of course, even if how you quantified footprint (using emissions per dollar or per pound estimates) and how you're quantifying improvement (actual project implementation) are out of sync.

In practice, companies have become comfortable using approaches A and B to set the baseline, and quantify savings through a completely different process. So, you estimate your total footprint one way, you calculate the benefits of improvements another way, and you still want the improvement numbers to equal the right percentage of reduction from the baseline, as dictated by your reduction goal. Organizations like the Gold Standard have been working to articulate a process to address these issues, find ways to intervene in supply chains, drive improvements, and make credible Scope 3 improvement claims through interventions.[5] Emerging guidance on this front encourages companies to gather primary data on their value chains (approach C), but a great many companies do not yet have the level of supply chain transparency required for that best practice work. Companies should gather supply chain data in parallel with approaches A/B to be able to apply approach C in the future

On the big picture of real-world GHG benefit, advancing GHG reductions with key suppliers is clearly great work to move forward, irrespective of measurability toward the baseline. You measure the

GHG benefit itself. The fact we have different measurement approaches between baseline and benefits is certainly less than ideal on my read, but it's acceptable, for now. In any event, whether or not you use different approaches, make sure your methods allow you to track progress toward your goals.

Set targets

> American corporations must continue to lead the way in driving efficiency, advancing a spectrum of low to negative emissions technologies and reducing GHG emissions.
>
> – Business Roundtable

Under science-based targets, companies with baseline inventory in hand voluntarily set dramatic GHG emission reduction targets for the next 5–15 years, as a reflection of the dramatic global emission reductions that need to happen in the world over the next 10–20 years.

SBTs require you, as a company, to come up with targets for your Scope 1 and Scope 2 emissions. Under SBTs, you must also apply a target to Scope 3 if your supply chain emissions are significant. (Spoiler alert: for most of your organizations, supply chain will be significant and you will need a target for Scope 3.)

Note that the purpose of SBTs is to drive real operational improvements, so you can't simply keep with business as usual and buy carbon offsets elsewhere, a strategy that companies will commonly use to make progress toward climate neutrality goals: planting trees, investing in renewables, and/or undertaking any number of offset project types elsewhere. Benefits need to happen within your operations and supply chain.

You can't hit the bullseye when the target is missing: the problem with 1.5°

Another important function of SBTs is to make alignment with science understandable. One problem with communications among the international climate science community is that the way they express targets doesn't translate well to company action.

Those gathered in December 2015 at the Conference of the Parties (COP) 21 in Paris achieved a historic agreement on how much fundamental atmospheric alteration the nations of the world are willing to accept. Subsequent COPs have focused on how to chart our best path forward as a global community. Core to this discussion are goals and targets. One central goal that has emerged is limiting the increase in global temperatures to 1.5°C. The big-picture thinking of the scientists and policymakers involved articulates the real outcomes we need to see in climate action.

However, I have an issue with the focus on 1.5° as a target. That issue is that the degrees leading up to the target are a metric that's actionable by neither the countries involved, nor the businesses that could support countries to achieve their goals.

Temperature is not something an individual nation or business can adjust. There's no clear pathway for China, the United States, or anyone else to reduce degrees of future warming. All businesses and nations can do is go forth with their activities and 30 or 80 years later hope to see in climate monitoring that, yes, indeed, global temperature only increased 1.4°. (We're already on the verge of missing the EV bus on keeping temperature increase below this level, but I digress.)

Better as a business metric is reduction of GHG emissions. Science-based targets do exactly that translation, offering a specific % reduction of GHG per year. However, it takes some digging to find a helpful benchmark. When working on my first SBT project, I waded through the documentation, learning how SBTs ask companies to set targets that are at least in line with degrees of temperature change. "Degrees of temperature are not what I care about." I thought, "Just tell me by how much we need to reduce emissions." Finally, buried on page 21 of the manual, I found what I was looking for:

1.5°: **4.2%**/year reduction
Well below 2°: **2.5%**/year reduction

Those reduction numbers show the minimum thresholds to achieve the 1.5° scenario. The target translates to a 50% reduction in GHG emissions by 2032 from a 2020 baseline.

If you want to make that clearer than "GHG emissions," and you haven't yet calculated your GHG emissions, set a goal like eliminating 70% of fossil fuel combustion by 2030 and 100% by 2040. Fossil fuel is clearly measured on our gas station receipts and utility bills, and it is clearly known to be the major contributor to the climate crisis.

As a business, you should certainly translate the known gallons, kWh, and therms into $MTCO_2E$ so you understand your footprint, including non-fossil fuel contributors as well as fossil fuel. You have to include all major GHG sources under virtually all programs that care about GHG. With a fossil fuel reduction goal, I'm simply saying that calling out fossil fuel combustion is very tangible and understandable, lending itself to a clear goal. Nail the commitment to 100% reduction and commit resources to that path.

Other emissions in our supply chains that are major contributors to the crisis come from land use (GHG flux from wetlands/forests, releases from agriculture soils, etc.). Those contributors are also more challenging to measure because impacts like nitrogen fertilizers on soil, deforestation, and methane impacts from rice farming can vary greatly, depending on local factors, and measurements don't neatly arrive on a utility bill. Even with those challenges, it remains crucially important to consider these contributors. It is an emerging practice to incorporate land use emissions in our GHG accounting.

Net zero goals allow for minimal burning of fossil fuels within your organizational boundaries, if there's a solid investment in renewables or other means to offset fossil use. Going all-electric in your buildings and generating as much renewable electricity as you take from the grid is one approach, typically in new buildings. Generating more renewable electricity than you take from the grid to offset any natural gas use in your buildings is another. Though there is often a lack of clarity around the extent to which fossil fuel use is allowed, the general net zero direction is helpful while we sort out ensuring real reductions.

The overall goal of 1.5° makes complete sense to the scientific community as a measure of climate alteration. However, it is critical that the big picture goal is translated to measures that are actionable at more local levels, for business and beyond.

Ambition

SBTs want you to be ambitious! Within SBTs, ambition is still framed in terms of degrees with SBTs, but we now have the translation.

Scopes 1 and 2: You need at least 2.5% reduction per year from your baseline. 4.2% reduction per year is the more ambitious and encouraged goal that may yet become the minimum standard. And that reduction is in absolute emissions. No matter how much you grow your business, emissions need to keep going down. Electricity procurement allows for some creativity with Scope 2 reduction, and allows you the option of purchasing credit for renewable electricity generated elsewhere.

Scope 3: There's more flexibility with Scope 3. "Intensity" targets allow you to adjust for growth (for example, reduce your emissions per pound of product) versus absolute targets that simply look at how much your baseline has been reduced, irrespective of business activity. The % Scope 3 reduction per year required, if an absolute target rather than an intensity target, is currently 1.2%. And you currently need to take responsibility for at least two-thirds of your Scope 3 emissions, leaving you flexibility to choose where to focus, but still requiring the bulk of emissions to be accounted for.

To stay apprised of ambition developments, bookmark www.sciencebasedtargets.org.

Alignment

I was discussing the SBT process with a sustainability manager at an apparel company. At one point, she said, "it's clear what's needed to be done. The challenge isn't the target setting, the challenge is implementing the plan." I was surprised. Can you just put numbers out in public view, make a company commitment to them, and not at least partially validate how close you'll get to the target with planned actions? I'm glad they found the courage to set the target, yet not deliberating about how ambitious of a target to set is problematic. Yes, the logic of SBT is clear to anyone concerned about climate. Yes, the GHG reduction work over a decade is clearly where so much of the effort is going to lie. And, yes, for most organizations, a certain amount of faith is required, given the unknowns that are involved. If you already knew how to reduce your emissions 30% or 50%, you probably would have done it and/ or would have a plan to do so, given climate is now clearly a priority to so many stakeholders. But to not plan out what you'll need to do is at best inconsiderate of your coworkers who will be asked to make significant efforts toward the target. At worst, it'll be a failure to achieve the reductions you seek and lead to a PR disaster.

To help a U.S.-based manufacturing client develop their climate strategy, vet actions and validate goals, I built a model to project the impacts of climate actions over the next decade, and to anticipate how close they'd come to the target. An example emissions trend is shown in Figure 2.3 (check out the beautifully downward sloping curve!).

Assuming you'll need credibility to sell SBT commitment within your company, I have to believe you'll need to go through a similar process to help all relevant departments understand what

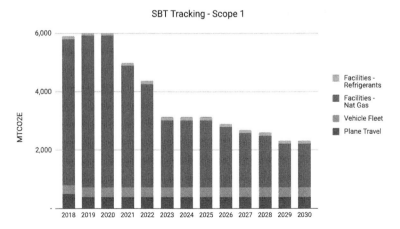

Figure 2.3 SBT Tracking.
Source: Author.

is the commitment and what is being asked of them. What you need to do is:

1. Identify what climate-friendly actions you're taking
2. Identify when those actions will happen
3. Identify price tag and the extent to which actions pay back for themselves over their lifetime
4. Quantify the impact on emissions over time

In addition to charting emissions, you should also chart out the investments that will be required in efficiency, renewables, and more, working with the decision-making departments involved: engineering, operations, procurement, logistics, and others. You'll be able to see the capital expenditures and financial returns as well as GHG trajectory. Investment is a crucial part of the conversation.

The vetting process points to collaboratively working across departments in your company. Ultimately, it'll be a subset of leadership that makes the decision on target, in most cases, but leaders in well-managed companies generally want to know that those charged with implementation have the capacity and resources to implement. Align through collaboration and make your future success that much more probable.

Notes

1 GHG Protocol (GHGP), "Corporate Standard", GHGP, 2004. http://www.ghgprotocol.org
2 The Intergovernmental Panel on Climate Change, "Reports", IPCC, 2020. https://www.ipcc.ch/reports/?rp=ar6
3 GHG Protocol, "Corporate Value Chain (Scope 3) Accounting and Reporting Standard", World Resources Institute and World Business Council for Sustainable Development, 2013.
4 U.S. EPA, "US Environmentally-Extended Input-Output (USEEIO) Technical Content", U.S. EPA, 2017. https://www.epa.gov/land-research/us-environmentally-extended-input-output-useeio-technical-content
5 Gold Standard, "Value Change", Gold Standard, 2020. https://www.goldstandard.org/impact-quantification/value-chain-interventions

Chapter 3

Reduce GHG! The saga continues

> We need to get to zero net greenhouse gas emissions in every
> sector of the economy within 50 years—and . . . we need to be
> on a path to doing it in the next 10 years.
>
> – Bill Gates

From measurement of climate impacts, we move onto reduction
of those climate impacts, and the content of what you do to bring
GHG emissions down, so your measurements start to show the
results that you wish to see.

As you work through this section of climate solutions, keep asking yourself these questions:

- Is this solution truly reducing GHGs in the air, whether eliminating emissions, reducing the rate of emissions, or removing
  the GHG that's already in the air?
- Are there multiple benefits from the climate solution? Does
  it improve biodiversity, contribute to social justice, or create
  other benefits? Or does it solely focus on reducing GHG in
  the air?
- For solutions that involve carbon removal (to be defined later),
  how permanent is the solution's GHG removal? Is there risk
  that captured carbon will be re-released back into the air?

Before getting into reduction details, however, let's segue to the
big picture.

DOI: 10.4324/9781003191544-4

Carbon is impressively maligned, considering it's a simple element in the periodic table, and responsible for all life on the planet. We clearly do not have a problem with the element itself. We celebrate carbon as a key component of all beings. The problem is the sudden increase of its most oxidized form (CO_2) in our atmosphere, when we and much of life have comfortably evolved with lower levels of CO_2 around.

It turns out we have nine limits on a planetary level, as articulated by the Stockholm Resilience Center. As depicted in Figure 3.1, four of them have been exceeded as of 2015 (in zones of uncertainty), three were deemed in the safe zone (innermost safe circle), and two were unknown.

In the intervening years since 2015, we've seen enough climate impacts to deem climate change further into the zone of uncertainty, and a 2018 UN report is in agreement with the spirit of that assessment, calling for a 45% drop in emissions by 2030.[1] Clearly, genetic diversity and nitrogen pollution in water are also critical. Planetary boundaries highlight the need to remain aware of other issues that demand attention, even with our focus on climate.

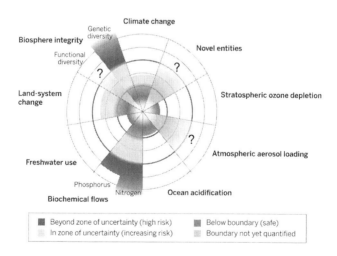

Figure 3.1 Planetary Boundaries.
Source: Planetary Boundaries, 2015, Science 347; Stockholm Resilience Centre.

These specific issues are as important as issues get! The safe limit we've transcended to move out of the safe zone on climate is the CO_2 limit of 350 ppm in the atmosphere.

Considering the history of life on the planet, given the variation of CO_2 levels over a long timeframe, my concern as it relates to climate is less about the actual level at a given time and much more about the rate of change. Though steep spikes in CO_2 did occur in the past, as shown in Figure 3.2, they're not literally vertical like the spike of the last 100 years that has transported us into CO_2 levels not seen in the last million years. The rate of change we've seen in the last 100 years, combined with what we project for the next 100, is unprecedented.

Unprecedented change calls for an unprecedented response. We have to reverse the dramatic climate snap at the end of that chart, like the Avengers of the Marvel Cinematic Universe who sought to reverse the actions of their foe, Thanos, who amassed enough power to wipe out half the life in the universe with a snap of his finger. We don't have the luxury of waiting for the Avengers (though if you find them, I definitely need to speak with Tony Stark!).

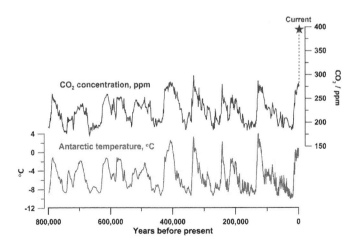

Figure 3.2 CO_2 versus Temperature.
Source: Healthy Planet U.K., CC BY SA 4.0 license.

The unleashing of the climate crisis is our challenge of heroic proportions. If we respond strategically to that crisis, we just might at least partially address other planetary issues, like biodiversity loss and nitrogen pollution, and unleash other co-benefits of climate action, like air pollution reduction and social justice.

The highest priority impacts for you to tackle depend on the results of your GHG accounting, but prominent classes of reduction actions throughout your value chain include:

- Efficiency—buildings
- Efficiency—transportation
- Renewable energy
- Refrigerant management

Efficiency and renewable energy actions represent a significant portion of your effort to reverse the snap. Placing those actions into a GHG reduction sequence for businesses, where the most logical actions to implement first are actually implemented first, looks like:

- Invest in process redesign to avoid unnecessary energy demand
- Invest in efficiency in facilities and fleets
  - LEDs, heat recovery, HVAC control upgrades, variable frequency drives on variable load motors, building shell insulation, sealing HVAC ducts, etc.
- Install renewables
  - Options include solar PV, solar thermal, wind, hydropower, geothermal, anaerobic digestion, organic waste-to-energy, and tidal
- Purchase clean energy through utility
- Explore Power Purchase Agreements (PPAs). As one primary way that PPAs manifest, renewable developers build and own solar or wind on your site, and sell you the electricity

A handful of these actions have established costs and payback, like solar and wind where the hours of sun and speed of wind are known (or can be measured) for a given location, and the costs of installation are relatively fixed. Returns on investment into other actions depend on the context. How often is equipment operating? How much energy waste are we preventing? In exploring the best investment opportunities among these actions, two questions come up:

- Where can we significantly reduce GHG emissions?
- Where do we get the best GHG reduction bang for our buck?

Reduce significant GHG sources

The quantification of Scope 1/Scope 2/Scope 3 we did earlier helps address the first question, pointing to where your largest GHG contributors are. What you don't yet know is the impact of any actions, and whether an action will reduce emissions by 10% or 50%. Pretend your emissions are those shown in Figure 3.3. Scope 1 totals 6% of total emissions, Scope 2 is 22%, and Scope 3 is the remainder. This chart also shows that you were able to collect electricity information from your supply chain, so it shows up in Scope 3 as well as in Scope 2. Electricity as a category across Scopes 2 and 3 represents 42% of total emissions, making it a prime candidate for reductions.

In gathering more details about the sites that use electricity, we can look at geography to help us prioritize further. Most fuels we

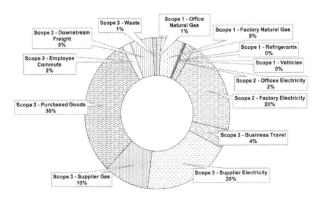

Figure 3.3 GHG Doughnut Chart.
Source: Author

use are location-agnostic in their GHG emissions. That is to say, burning a gallon of gasoline in the United States has the same footprint as burning that gallon of gasoline in Japan or in Sudan.

With electricity, the impact of using 1 kWh all depends on what goes into the grid in that area to make that kWh—coal, natural gas, hydro, renewables, or nuclear—so not all electricity is created equally. Within different areas of the United States ("NERC subregions" in electric grid geek dialect, where the subregions reflect how electricity is managed and often span states), some electricity is cleaner than others, as illustrated and partially annotated in the EPA eGRID[2] subregions map in Figure 3.4. In Canada, GHG intensity is reported by province, and in Europe, emission factors for electricity are reported by country.

The largest benefit of efficiency is seen in the dirtiest grids, where you avoid the dirtiest electricity. The dirtiest grids are tagged with the number corresponding to the pounds of CO_2-equivalent generated for each MWh of electricity produced. In the United States,

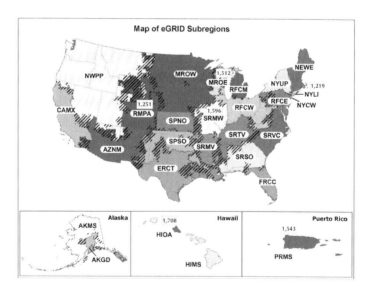

Figure 3.4 U.S. eGRID Map.
Source: U.S. EPA, eGRID map, with author annotations.

grids in the upper Midwest, in the Rockies and on islands currently stand out, though grid cleanliness changes over time as the mix of energy sources shifts.

Get the best bang for your buck

It's not enough to simply understand the magnitude of GHG impact. We also want to understand the financials to make informed investment decisions, leading us into the second question around bang for your buck. Efficiency is commonly said to be the cheapest source of energy, freeing up energy to be used elsewhere instead of adding generation to provide energy. In addition, efficiency is the second action, after redesign, within the energy GHG reduction hierarchy presented earlier. Within efficiency, different measures have different ROI. Repairs such as plugging the leaks in an electricity-intensive HVAC system will generally have a great return. LED lighting and controls, if properly calibrated and commissioned, have historically shown quick paybacks in commercial buildings when replacing less efficient lighting.

So, projects like lighting retrofits and HVAC repair in the dirtiest grids emerge as our lead opportunity. (I'm looking at you, Illinois-Missouri!) You can take a similar approach to your business. If you have several sites across the nation, geographic analytics around electricity can help you target facility improvements in terms of climate goals, though clearly other considerations like facility age, equipment age, and capital budgets should also come into play.

There are several points of constraint in our fossil fuel use that will take concerted effort to overcome. Electricity use is relatively simple to shift away from GHG-intensive coal and natural gas, as so many renewable energies are in the form of electricity, and thus, electrification of gas equipment is now a popular strategy. Building designers are getting the profession to a place where buildings can reliably be built net zero in a relatively affordable manner. Other areas that require some creativity include the following:

- Industrial process heating based on natural gas. The high concentration of energy required for activities like forging metal becomes a challenge in seeking alternatives. One alternative getting attention is hydrogen, which can be generated from renewable electricity. Expect more "renewable hydrogen" to come into the world with further solar proliferation, as one way to store excess power during peak sun hours is to use that power to create hydrogen. Another potential solution for industrial heating supported by investors like Bill Gates is concentrated solar.[3]

- Financing to make efficiency and renewables even more affordable. Yes, renewables are now the cheapest form of electricity, but there are still too many reasons to not retrofit existing facilities. We need to get to a place where the renewable economics are irresistible. The solution could well involve eliminating remaining subsidies for fossil fuels and applying a price on carbon, requiring the policy advocacy we touched on earlier, as those actions go beyond the ability of any one business to enact. You can use a price on carbon for internal investment decisions for your company, and I recommend you do so as a good practice. What that entails is understanding your GHG emission sources, and in any projects (infrastructure, equipment, or other) under consideration that change those GHG emissions, factor in a price on carbon. For example, if the project increases your electricity demand at $0.10/kWh, then factor in not only the higher direct costs of electricity, but also the carbon footprint of that electricity at $15 or $50 per metric ton of CO_2e emitted. A fuller discussion of price on carbon lies ahead.

- Baseload for the electric grid. This is more of an issue for the power grid operator than individual businesses, but the intermittency of renewables means that for grid reliability, a more constant energy source is needed. Currently, that's primarily supplied by natural gas, nuclear, large hydro, and coal. Renewable energy storage is the focus of forward-thinking grid designers and businesses looking beyond their own boundaries for solutions. In addition to the resurgence of interest in hydrogen generated by using excess renewables, solutions include battery storage and other technologies (pumped hydro, compressed air, thermal storage, etc.), but we're not there yet on implementation. Action on grid resilience might be mostly out of your hands, but it's good to have on your radar.

Other reduction pathways to tackle include the following.

Scopes 1 and 2

Renewable electricity, continued

Wind and solar are great investments with the drop in installation costs, particularly solar over the past decade. You will see under a 10-year payback in many markets, with a 25+ year lifetime (so back of the envelope says you get 2.5 times your initial investment back, minus maintenance investments and any generation deterioration, and not discounting future cash flow). This payback may be longer than other investments that you can make, but consider how many other investments you willingly make in your business—whether advertising, business development activities, or other—that may have no measurable return and/or where no one asks what the ROI is. The financial assets you have invested in a stock market index fund might net a 7% annual return. Returns on renewables are at least as good in many cases, and if renewable assets are less liquid than your mutual fund holdings, the vagaries of the stock market can be at least as risky as renewables.

To get a first-order approximation of solar system size needed and savings for a given building, the National Renewable Energy Laboratory (NREL) offers the PVWatts[TM] tool.[4] Enter your location, a guess at system size, and the cost of your electricity, and it'll give you the amount of solar production in kWh as well as savings. Divide that solar production number by the system size in kW to back calculate the hours of solar available at your location. Divide your building's total electricity demand by that number of hours, and you arrive at a rough system size for your building. Example input is depicted in Figure 3.5.

For wind and solar financial modeling, NREL also offers the System Advisor Model, which allows you to adjust an array of installation cost, debt, interest rates, depreciation, and other parameters to calculate payback time as accurately as you can.´

Resources also include U.S. Wind Turbine Database, a map-based database where you can point and click to review operating wind turbines in your area: height, power production, make, model, and year.[5] Gaps shown in Figure 3.6 don't necessarily mean

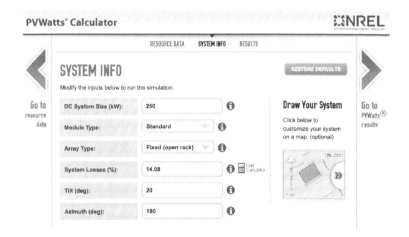

Figure 3.5 NREL PVWatts.
Source: National Renewable Energy Lab, pvwatts.nrel.gov.

Figure 3.6 U.S. Wind Turbine Map.
Source: U.S. Geological Survey, eerscmap.usgs.gov/uswtdb.

wind power can't be done in those areas, and just means that it hasn't been done yet! The upper Great Plains generally has the best potential in the United States.

The availability of solar and wind is broad, even if some areas have more potential than others. Renewables beyond solar and wind tend to be more location-specific. For example, whether you have geothermal or tidal potential depends on your proximity to high potential areas. NREL also assessed dams throughout the United States where hydropower could feasibly be added,[6] as shown in Figure 3.7, and illustrated how creative thinking can help develop resources where none are apparent. Other creative ideas include harvesting vibrational energy from roadways, gym equipment, or even dance floors, but I've yet to see anything at scale.

As referenced earlier, we also need renewable energy storage to have renewables available when the sun isn't shining and the wind

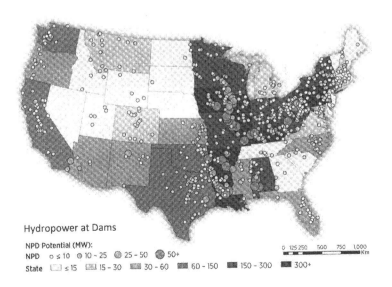

Figure 3.7 Hydropower Map.
Source: National Renewable Energy Laboratory, atb.nrel.gov.

isn't blowing. The Department of Energy Global Storage Database documents a range of battery, pumped hydro, hydrogen, compressed air, and thermal storage options that individual facilities, companies, and utilities are using to store renewables.[7] Leading companies looking to hit climate goals will increasingly need to advance storage one way or another, whether at their own facilities or advocating for grid storage.

Renewable natural gas (NG)

Electricity isn't the only type of renewable energy, though it takes a great deal of the focus. Electrification—shifting natural gas to electricity—is often a recommended carbon strategy, but there are applications, particularly industrial processes, where that isn't easy. The methane we combust in natural gas typically comes from petroleum sources, but there are other sources. Landfills, wastewater treatment plants, and large livestock operations all generate waste that can be used to generate methane, capture it, clean it up, and put it into a pipeline. Where there's a will, there's a way. Get the power of manure to work for you! Note one challenge in many cases is that you're unlikely to be close enough to the source to power your facility directly, so you are likely instead to pay to clean up methane, have it placed into a more distant pipeline, and get credit for the effort. Expect renewable NG to be a growing practice as companies tackle their Scope 1 emissions, and encounter barriers to electrification.

Fleet vehicles

At vehicle replacement time, plug-in hybrids, EVs, and conventional hybrids should be considered. The $5K–$15K premium over conventional isn't generally completely paid for in fuel savings with current gas prices. Factor in the value of hitting climate goals, though, and an internal price on carbon, and you're there. One of the larger selling points for EVs now is saved maintenance costs.[8] Look over the life cycle of the asset at first costs, maintenance costs, fuel costs, and the social cost of carbon to make an informed decision.

Low GWP refrigerants

One pound of leaked refrigerant typically has 1–2 tons of CO_2-equivalent impact! In any new construction and/or cooling systems, choice of HVAC systems should consider those with low global warming potential refrigerants, like ammonia, propane, isopentane, and even CO_2. Ironically, our major GHG can be used as refrigerant, and has a global warming potential that is 1,000–3,000 times lower than typical refrigerants. Leaders on the clean refrigerant front include grocery stores Aldi[9] and Whole Foods.[10] Unfortunately, it's not straightforward to substitute a different refrigerant in your existing system, as different systems are designed for different gases and very low GWP refrigerants are generally very different chemicals than HFCs.

Note that in focusing on reducing footprint, I'm intentionally leaving out (1) renewable energy credits (RECs) and (2) carbon offsets, which allow you to buy credit and/or carbon removal against your Scope 1 and Scope 2 footprint, but don't reduce it directly. More on that later.

Scope 3

Sourcing/procurement

Greening

Key supplies used by your business may currently be GHG intensive, but that's not necessarily a reason to not use them. Work instead with the supplier to incorporate the measures above into their own operations and reduce the GHG intensity of those supplies.

Substitution

Where that supplier work doesn't get you the results you want, look at less GHG-intensive alternatives. Decision points where this is relevant are in choices of building materials, supplies that are certified to avoid deforestation, and suppliers that have committed to source renewable energy to make their products.

Packaging

Both Greening and Substitution procurement actions apply here, as you can work with your packaging supplier. Incorporating recycled content into packaging is huge, as the packaging footprint of many manufacturing companies eclipses their Scope 1 + Scope 2 footprint. Be aware that packaging decisions must take into account compostability, not just climate impacts, to avoid long-term plastic pollution problems. Innovations include Ecovative's mushroom mycelium-based substitute for Styrofoam,[11] biodegradable films from Mango Materials,[12] and FullCycle Bioplastics[13] created from organic waste! Earlier, biobased plastics were stated to be generally less GHG intensive than petroleum-based plastics, and you can use that as a general guide, but still do your homework and ask packaging providers to tell you what they know about the carbon footprint of their products.

Freight

Shift to rail and marine

Sending freight by rail and sea can reduce freight footprint by over 75% compared with road, according to the U.K.'s Department of Business[14] and the U.S. EPA.[15] Use of rail and sea freight can involve more upfront planning compared with road, and at 75% GHG savings, use of those modes is worth some planning effort.

Aerodynamic improvements

For freight that remains on the road, a suite of aerodynamic improvement measures help with truck efficiency: boat tails, underbody devices, and more. In addition to improving fuel use, how incredibly cool is it to drop that you're using vortex generators?[16]

Business travel

Planes

Alternative energies for flight are admittedly tough. United Airlines has committed to greater biofuel use,[17] and Airbus indicated ten years ago they were looking at electrification,[18] yet flight remains on traditional jet fuel. There are rumors of hydrogen-powered flight, but that's not yet close to reality, and that's only good if the hydrogen is sourced from renewables. In the interim, best to harness the web conferencing technology so many discovered during the COVID-19 pandemic, and limit flights to mission-critical needs.

Cars

For fleets you own, www.fueleconomy.gov is there to help you out, among the plethora of guidance from other sources. Mass transit is often not considered for business travel to and/or within other cities (e.g. when you fly elsewhere, how often do you look into taking bus or rail from the airport?), but if you're traveling through an urban or suburban setting, look into it!

Even more remains to explore, but the above captures a wide range of opportunities to tackle your footprint. Take on the totality of these reduction actions, and you and your business become real-world Avengers in reversing the climate snap.

Working the land

> It would be better if we mitigated the effects of global warming and had cleaner air in our cities and weren't drilling for vast amounts of coal, oil and gas in parts of the world that are problematic and will run out anyway.
>
> – Elon Musk

The theme of the previous section is clear: reduce emissions into the air. The other part of the equation to reduce CO_2 levels is to remove the carbon that's already in the air. Methods to do so involve:

- Capturing carbon in soils through agriculture
- Allowing and encouraging nature and natural systems to remove CO_2 from the air
- Carbon removal technology, or "climatetech"

All methods should be at least considered as part of your climate action toolbox, tapping into the promise of soil, the power of nature, and the carbon removal innovation that may well play a support role. Land-based climate solutions like protecting nature and building soil are particularly relevant if your business touches on food and fiber supply chains, but even if not, if you're a landowner, you have the potential to host solutions. Agriculture and land use represent roughly a quarter of all GHG emissions, and we can't talk about climate solutions without talking about agriculture.

The new cash crop

Emerging out of the mysterious and shadowy places that host soil science discussions and stepping into the limelight is carbon farming. Carbon farming uses agriculture to build soil carbon through drawing carbon out of the air. Being in the limelight comes with hyperbolic claims about the potential of carbon farming. What really is the promise? How do we enable farming to redistribute carbon from air to soil?

Five practices that help capture carbon in soil[19] are highlighted in the Inside Climate News infographic in Figure 3.8. These measures should not look new. The USDA's Natural Resources Conservation Service (NRCS) has been promoting at least a few of these practices for decades.

The Carbon Cycle Institute highlights over 25 measures for landowners and farmers to promote carbon storage.[20] Measures like windbreaks and riparian restoration avoid wind and water erosion to avoid loss of the soil carbon that is already there. Other measures help actively build carbon in the soil, like multi-story cropping.

One point of contention is how long the carbon is stored. Do the increases we measure in the soil at the end of the growing season stay locked-in for decades, or is it ephemeral, re-released into the air through microbial or other action? Amanda Ravenhill of the Buckminster Fuller Institute speaks of the earth as "breathing" over the course of the year. Plant growth in the northern hemisphere takes up carbon in the spring, and releases it as plant matter decays in the fall. Much of that has to do with forests and the life

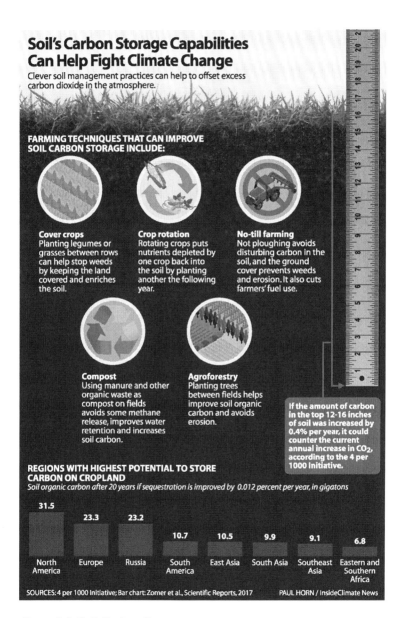

Figure 3.8 Soil Carbon Storage.
Source: Paul Horn/Inside Climate News.

cycle of leaves, not just farmland. Yet, we know soils release carbon as well as store it. "Labile" soil carbon is the fraction that breaks down quickly and gets released, which includes much of the new annual carbon represented by plant growth. According to the organization Soil Quality, in some farming and soil type regimes, soil carbon concentration over years can change very little.[21] This in part flies in the face of the regenerative agriculture practices that we just looked at.

That's why measurement and outcome-based approaches are critical. Given complex soil dynamics and many different soil microclimates, actually gauging what soil carbon is present and how it changes over time is crucial. Dictating proven practices has its place, but measurement is the real path for verification, helping to answer three questions:

- How much carbon is in the soil now?
- By how much can we increase carbon content and maintain soil health?
- How fast can we get carbon into the soil, without disrupting its other ecological functions?

Green America's Center for Sustainability Solutions and NSF unveiled a verification standard[22] to ensure any regenerative agriculture efforts actually sequester the carbon that they purport to sequester. The international 4 Per 1,000 Initiative has the goal to increase soil carbon by 0.4% (thus, four parts per one thousand) per year, which by their math would halt the annual increase in GHG emissions. In the many places where soil carbon has been lost, regeneration is a no-brainer on concept, if a some-brainer on approach.

To help capture those benefits, the carbon farming industry in Australia (when it comes back around, happy National Regenerative Agriculture Day to those down under![23]) now has a roadmap for implementation, coming at the issue from a market perspective. With extreme droughts and wildfire risks, regenerative agriculture is seen as a potential savior to help mitigate those impacts. If markets are generating money for carbon farming, as highlighted in the Australian roadmap, that's welcome. However, those investing money in carbon farming to reduce their GHG footprint, whether voluntarily through markets or because of regulation, must actively be reducing their emissions to be successful. Reducing emissions will drop that 4 per 1,000 number to 3 or 2 per 1,000, and make achieving carbon balance that much easier.

Regarding the amount by which we can increase soil carbon, 2% soil carbon is often referenced as a carbon level in soils. That's 20,000 ppm. Four per 1,000 is equivalent to 4,000 ppm. Compare that with the 60 ppm of CO_2 that we're told we need to draw out of the atmosphere, and you see the orders of magnitude of greater potential concentration in soil. Carbon can be much more concentrated in soil, while contributing to soil health for plant and microbial life.

We need to talk about rates of removal and understand how fast we can increase soil carbon. Knowing the total percentage of soil carbon doesn't tell you whether it takes one year or 1,000 years to get there. Studies suggest 1.6–3.2 metric tons of carbon/acre/year[24] from perennial agriculture. Marin Carbon Project reports roughly 1 ton/acre/year from compost application to grasslands. Perhaps the seminal work on the topic, *The Carbon Farming Solution* by Eric Toensmeier, details a range of carbon removal potentials among many crops, climates, and landscapes. Tools to help gauge the impact of farming and ranching include COMET-Farm[25] and Cool Farm Tool,[26] allowing farms to provide an array of inputs and details on their soil type and management techniques to get estimates on the greenhouse gas benefits of their practices.

Carbon farming as a solution is worthy of serious investment by food processors, government agriculture agencies, the investor community, and, of course, farmers. Forums like the Regenerative Earth Summit,[27] the Soil and Climate Alliance (the group formerly known as the Carbon Farming Innovation Network),[28] and NoRegrets Initiative[29] are working on those fronts, but much more work is needed. Success requires collaboration through the entire supply chain to make it happen. Better than supply chain, think of it as a supply cycle where value from customer comes back to the farm.

As a purchaser, *your business can encourage your suppliers to incorporate carbon farming techniques and measure the results to gauge the impact of the effort.*

In addition to questions of "how much?" and "how fast?" it's even more important to ask "where?" that farming should most wisely take place, and on what types of landscapes and soils.

Application of compost to grasslands has been shown to sequester carbon.[30] However, where those grasslands are natural grasslands that have not been recently cultivated, compost application would alter the ecosystem that already exists. In theory, undisturbed land could be used to accelerate carbon uptake, but in reality that seems a poor choice, given we benefit from grassland ecosystem services.

Thus, we should be focusing our regenerative agriculture efforts on degraded lands. For example:

- Existing agricultural lands where soil carbon has been depleted
- Abandoned industrial and commercial lands in suburban and rural areas, where legacy pollution is not a concern
- Mining-disturbed landscapes in need of reclamation, if appropriate for agriculture

Clearcut forest is also disturbed land, but efforts there should focus on reforestation, with all its associated benefits (carbon, habitat, air, water filtration and purification, etc.). What we should not be doing is damaging healthy ecosystems to practice regenerative agriculture, as nature provides climate benefits, too.

Make your investments in food and fiber systems count. Leverage that purchasing for better climate outcomes.

Livestock: environmental scourge or climate savior?

> Only when we see that we are part of the totality of the planet, not a superior part with special privileges, can we work effectively to bring about an earth restored to wholeness.
>
> – Elizabeth Watson

In addition to carbon farming, animal agriculture also deserves discussion.

There's been real dissonance on the climate impacts of livestock. For decades, we've heard about the massive GHG impacts of industrial livestock agriculture, and that you're better off raising a variety of grains and legumes and feeding humans directly, rather than using animals as a protein middleman (middle being?). That's particularly true where food crops that could serve as human food are instead fed to livestock.

Plenty of recent studies raise cautionary notes on livestock, particularly cattle and sheep, where the methane that is generated in their bodies (enteric, in researcher lingo) makes them one of the highest GHG sources of nutrition that there are, even per kg of protein, as documented by the website Our World in Data[31] among other sources and depicted in Figure 3.9.

However, newer thinking holds out livestock as a solution, indicating that grazing invigorates the growth of grasses, which helps capture carbon in soil. Properly managed grazing also generates manure in amounts that can be assimilated by local soils. This is

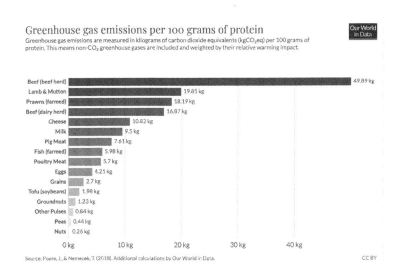

Figure 3.9 Our World in Data.
Source: Hannah Ritchie and Max Roser, OurWorldInData.org, CC BY 4.0 license. Based on Poore, J., & Nemecek, T. (2018).

relevant where livestock are grass-fed rather than held in feedlots. Livestock and many other animals transform marginal-for-farming lands and inedible-by-humans plant life into quality protein.

Who's right? If the new thinking is indeed the case, why do rangelands so often look depleted? What percentage of livestock are actually raised in ways that make them a climate solution? And how does a business sourcing from livestock farms intervene to help make this happen?

Let's first explain the origins of the key livestock product of GHG concern—beef. According to Ohio State University, roughly 20% of beef comes from dairy cattle.[32] Dairy cattle that provide milk and related products are typically concentrated at farms. The beef cattle that are raised for meat could be concentrated on feedlots eating grain or could be on rangeland eating grass. Beef cattle are generally moved to grass after calves are weaned, and then move to feedlot in their last four to six months. The time between weaning and feedlot is the window of grazing opportunity for sequestering carbon on rangeland.

To get climate benefits in that life cycle, according to the Savory Institute, grazing should be managed to mimic wild grazing,[33] rather than concentrated in feedlots where those environmental impacts escalate. Managers use rotational grazing to make that happen. Benefits only happen if livestock are managed well. Decades of non-management of livestock for soil regeneration has resulted in depleted and overgrazed landscapes.

It's also important to consider the type of livestock being raised. If net carbon sequestration is to happen, the carbon removal benefit from enriched soils needs to be larger than the carbon equivalent from super pollutant methane generation. That's a tall order. The alternative to net carbon sequestration in the animals' process itself is to accept the methane load as a byproduct of a very promising way to rebuild soil carbon, and find ways to offset that load.

Research suggests seaweed as a feed additive can reduce methane production, with recent field tests suggesting a 30%–40% methane reduction. However, grazers have evolved in relationship with methanogenic microorganisms in their gut. Consider it their microbiome, should you be tracking the latest in human digestive health. Penn State researchers caution us about disrupting that microbial balance.[34] Yet Washington Post investigation suggests the disruption caused by specific types of seaweed helps the animal produce more milk and/or grow faster.[35] It's possible some methanogens aren't critical and are just along for the livestock gut ride, but it's complex. In any event, it's worth further investigation as to how you would encourage any source farms to use this feed practice.

Seaweed application helps address methane generated within the animal, but not the smaller yet significant source of methane from manure. There is evidence that composting manure fixes carbon more effectively than direct soil application of manure. Though that requires manure collection—implying animals are concentrated, rather than wandering the landscape like natural grazers—it can certainly be part of the solution at feedlots. In addition, direct soil application of manure can generate a potent third greenhouse gas—nitrous oxide (N_2O).[36] Nature has applied manure directly to soils for eons, but in an age where GHG emissions have become a critical issue, we would do well to look at the most effective ways to minimize emissions. Encouraging suppliers to incorporate composting, where applicable, is wise. An alternative is to incorporate anaerobic digestion and generate energy from manure. If not building soil carbon, you are capturing a super pollutant and using it to generate a form of clean energy.

The cattle have another factor leaning in their favor, and it's an important aspect of this debate which gets little attention. Emissions where the carbon comes from deep beneath the earth (fossil fuels) are different from the carbon that's already in the biosphere (plant and animal matter). In the GHG Protocol, companies report bioenergy emissions separately from fossil fuel–based emissions for this reason. Carbon already in the biosphere naturally cycles between different forms. CO_2 in the air is incorporated into plant matter, gets eaten by animals, becomes part of that animal for a while or excreted, possibly as methane or as other compounds, and often returns to CO_2.

That cycling of biogenic carbon, as embodied so well by livestock, ordinarily wouldn't be a concern, but we've brought up so much Carboniferous era carbon in the last 100 years that there's now too much carbon in the air, period, for Holocene types like us. Employment of livestock to build soil carbon needs to take their methane and manure impacts into account. That said, there may certainly be cases where livestock—particularly goats—are desirable for landscape management. Livestock and/or wild hooved animals will see a role in the carbon-sane future because they can help regenerate grasslands.

The flip side of carbon that naturally cycles within living systems is that the carbon trapped there isn't as permanently trapped as it was when locked away deep under the earth as fossil fuel. The conversion of former fossil fuel carbon into less permanent soil, tree and plant mass needs to be coupled with techniques that more permanently sequester the carbon away from the atmosphere and seas. Producing biochar is one approach to make the carbon more stable, heating woody biomass in the absence of oxygen. We looked earlier at the short-termism of soil carbon, where large fractions of carbon built up over the growing season get re-released into the air. For a business looking to employ carbon removal to reduce its footprint, understanding the permanence of carbon removal is crucial, and that is as true with animal agriculture as it is carbon farming.

The appearance of degraded land is one indicator of land health. More abundant lands have rich, dark soil and vibrant, diverse plant life. In general, with indicators, once you visualize what improvement looks like, you begin to see the possible. However, you also need to understand what pathways allow you to get to that improvement. Indicator + pathway holds the key to positive change. If you're in manufacturing rather than farming, quality management systems say essentially the same thing. For some innovative farmers, their path is now through Holistic Management, using animals with rotational grazing practices. Animal agriculture can actually be integrated with carbon farming, with farmers managing an ecosystem of crops and animals to get the best outcomes. Co-benefits include the animal welfare highlighted by Regenerative Organic Alliance, leading to happier and healthier animals.

Outside of regenerative agriculture, given an agricultural system that currently produces so much of our protein with concentrated feedlots and their significant environmental impacts, it is wise to explore our non-livestock means to create protein with relatively little GHG impact. Protein can be raised in a low-carbon way through many means:

- Expand use of tried-and-true legumes like soybeans and lentils that have fed people for millennia and have a low footprint per pound compared with most meats. Regeneratively raised livestock is currently all the rage, as a relatively new and exciting topic that's given new life to the sense of responsible meat, but given the very small percentage of meat that's actually raised that way, we'd do well to go back to basics and encourage plant-based eating until major agricultural shifts happen. If shifts happen, I suspect they will significantly drop the amount of meat available, with regenerative requiring a larger land base to avoid overgrazing.

- Raise fish and greens in closed-loop aquaponics systems, where fish manure is used as a plant nutrient and plants help purify the water that filters back to the fish.

- Source from free-range poultry that provide meat and eggs from the plants and bugs that people don't eat, and leave nutrients for crops that people do eat.

- Eat those bugs directly! Insects such as crickets and mealworms grow with near zero inputs, and are now snack options,[37, 38] if broad public acceptance might require some work.

- Plant-based lab-grown meats. As referenced earlier, Impossible Foods documents their Impossible Burger has 10% the GHG footprint of beef. Also consider sourcing and production in this emerging field to be clear that it's a good option for non-climate reasons.[39]

In your protein sourcing, consider these options.

Soil isn't just for carbon storage, of course. Soil needs to be healthy as measured by a range of other soil health indicators and nutrient levels. In ignoring that, our mindset toward disposing of carbon parallels our other approaches to handling "waste," where we sacrifice an area in the interests of waste disposal. Waste in this case is excess CO_2. In theory, we could create exceptionally high carbon levels in soil, or improperly fix the carbon, to where it interferes with other aspects of soil or groundwater health. I have yet to see scientific evidence of that concern, yet it's still good practice to be cautious with the mindset we have around throwing our problems "away" and repeating the waste management errors of the past. To be truly sustainable at a given site, agriculture needs to sustain the health of the water and soils that support it, and sustain the health of the plants and animals involved. The carbon cycle is just one component of agroecology, if a critical one, with cascades of nutrients, water, and carbon moving through different parts of the food web.

Your interventions in your fiber and farm supply chains should broadly take soil health into account, even if the focus of interventions is to build soil carbon. Think as holistically as the living systems from which you draw ingredients and feedstocks.

So done with farming. How else to remove carbon?

> The time to answer the greatest challenge of our existence on this planet is now. You can make history or be vilified by it.
> – Leonardo DiCaprio

We've talked a great deal about farming. It's an easy target, as it's an activity that affects an impressive portion of land on the planet. Small improvements over millions of acres add up. Beyond farming, another approach to remove carbon from the air is through habitat restoration and nature preservation.

#TheForgottenSolution

So much of the decades-long climate action focus has been on renewable energy and efficiency that at the Global Climate Action Summit of 2018 in San Francisco, nature was highlighted as #TheForgottenSolution. The Nature Conservancy (TNC) documented that nature is 20% of the climate footprint, but gets only 0.1% of the attention.[40] Forgotten indeed!

By "nature," they're referring to land use (or AFOLU in international climate-speak—agriculture, forests, and other land use). That land use is 24% of GHG emissions, according to the latest IPCC report.[41] TNC and a consortium of groups chronicled how forest loss has represented around 10% of emissions alone. Stemming from their work, Figure 3.10 illustrates that a suite of peatlands, seagrass, farmlands, and other natural areas could provide 37% of the climate

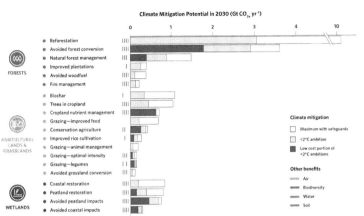

20 Pathways of Natural Climate Solutions

Climate Mitigation Potential in 2030 (Gt CO₂, yr⁻¹)

FORESTS
- Reforestation
- Avoided forest conversion
- Natural forest management
- Improved plantations
- Avoided woodfuel
- Fire management

AGRICULTURAL LANDS & GRASSLANDS
- Biochar
- Trees in cropland
- Cropland nutrient management
- Grazing—improved feed
- Conservation agriculture
- Improved rice cultivation
- Grazing—animal management
- Grazing—optimal intensity
- Grazing—legumes
- Avoided grassland conversion

WETLANDS
- Coastal restoration
- Peatland restoration
- Avoided peatland impacts
- Avoided coastal impacts

Climate mitigation
- Maximum with safeguards
- <2°C ambition
- Low cost portion of <2°C ambitions

Other benefits
- Air
- Biodiversity
- Water
- Soil

Climate mitigation potential and co-benefits of the different NCS pathways. Reproduced with permission from TNC and PNAS.

Figure 3.10 Natural Climate Solutions.
Source: The Nature Conservancy, adapted from PNAS.org October 31, 2017 figure. 114 (44) 11645-11650, doi.org/10.1073/pnas.1710465114.

solution.[42] Exciting! A large portion of that benefit comes from reforestation. And at least as exciting is that the costs for over half of that potential is less than $100/ton CO_2E, which is within the range of what's typically referred to as the "social cost of carbon". That is, the cost of mitigation is similar to the cost to society, and thus a worthy investment. That investment could be at least partially funded by the earlier price on carbon discussion.

While we're on the subject of social cost of carbon, let's clearly define it. The social cost of carbon is comprised of the social and environmental costs of the problems that are created every time a home, vehicle, or business emits a ton of CO_2 emissions—the economic disruption caused by the climate crisis and extreme weather crises, deleterious impacts in public health, the military costs of protecting fossil fuel interests, and more. In an honest carbon market, it's the amount we would have to pay for our emissions. However, no one is paying for these problems to be fixed directly, even if virtually everyone in more affluent nations is contributing to the problem. If the tab gets picked up, it's generally by the taxpayer.

People often ask about the price of action. They often don't ask about the price of *not* acting. And tragically so, as the first question is not meaningful if you don't ask the second. Context matters. You don't know whether one option is good or bad unless you have another option with which to compare. In this case, if you use TNC's $100/ton as the social cost, it costs more to *not* implement over half the natural climate solutions. If you use the $220–$260/ton social cost estimate from other researchers instead, even more solutions become affordable, because the price of climate inaction becomes that much higher.

Given that potential, why were natural climate solutions forgotten? In part, it has to do with the focus on fossil fuel as the prime contributor to the climate crisis, which leads you to focus on solutions that reduce fossil fuel. We have been more focused on reducing emissions into the air, for defensible reasons, than on removing emissions from the air. Non-natural technical solutions like LEDs and EVs also meet a direct need. Businesses, individuals, and institutions buy things with GHG impacts. If you can offer a substitute with lower GHG impact, like LEDs or EVs, your solution inserts relatively easily into a business's systems, as one form of market-based solutions. Your climate benefit is aligned with a customer need. Though many benefits are derived from nature, natural areas that comprise climate solutions aren't embedded in your operations in the same way, and are not something you buy directly for use in production, so you're less likely to buy natural climate solutions.

Nature was also forgotten due to lack of measurement. In managing businesses, we know and monitor the gallons of gasoline, the therms of natural gas, and the kWh of electricity that we're using. That measurement makes them visible as targets to reduce. With landscapes, there's not the same measurement and monitoring of water purification and carbon removal. Not visible is equivalent to being not a target to reduce. That makes it impossible to stay on target. And you don't know how much you've mangled understanding how much climate solutions that natural systems provide until you measure them, as TNC and partners discovered.

As a landowning business, you can play a role in helping nature be not forgotten.

Whether formally as part of carbon market mechanisms, or informally to track your benefits, there are ways to estimate carbon uptake in tree planting. The U.S. Forest Service has a tree carbon calculator to quantify the benefit of planting trees.[43] Trees—and nature broadly—are good examples of where we should be thinking holistically and beyond carbon. In addition to carbon uptake, trees offer wildlife habitat, heat island mitigation, shade, fruit/nut/ seed production, and other benefits.

Climate benefits of habitat restoration more broadly are harder to pin down. The U.S. Geological Service has tools to look at changes in carbon over time for bioregions,[44] but that does not translate well to looking at the per acre benefits of restoring prairie, meadow, and riparian zone. As of 2021, the GHG Protocol is developing guidance on the climate benefits of better land use[45] to help companies more reliably predict and report the benefits of land use actions. Start-up companies like Pachama and NCX (formerly SilviaTerra) are working with satellite-based monitoring to help understand land use changes and encourage land uses that result in high carbon removal.

We know there are benefits to nature preservation and enhancement, and we are crafting greater agreement on what those benefits are. In recognizing the conceptual power of science-based targets, the Science Based Targets Network is taking what SBTs have done with climate and expanding it to nature and biodiversity, with the end goal to provide guidance to businesses on how to align operations with the needs of ecosystems.[46]

In the interim, invest in ecosystem preservation and restoration. We often need to act in the face of uncertainty, and there's enough certainty around the value of nature to inspire its preservation and expansion.

ClimateTech

> Wisdom demands a new orientation of science and technology towards the organic, the gentle, the non-violent, the elegant, and the beautiful.
>
> – E. F. Schumacher

If you're not removing carbon naturally, then you're removing carbon unnaturally. That is, using human-engineered approaches to draw CO_2 out of the air. There is a range of tactics in the engineered carbon removal playbook. Terms you'll want to know:

Carbon capture and storage (CCS)

CCS is usually attributed to projects located at CO_2-rich exhaust streams like those at power plants. As the name suggests, the CO_2 generated from combustion is captured through some means and then stored out of the atmosphere, as shown in Figure 3.11. For those not wishing to change the existing energy system, it's attractive. Emit away with the established power plants, capture those emissions, and you're saving the atmosphere with relatively little pain in system redesign.

I have been skeptical of CCS for a while, and that's in thinking about carbon capture as a thermodynamics problem. CO_2 is the result of a combustion reaction that releases much energy. To get back to a different compound, you need to put in energy. If we were recreating the fuel, you'd have to put that much energy in and more, courtesy of entropy, and force those hydrogen atoms back onto the carbon. CO_2 is fully oxidized, which is not helpful for further chemical reactions. It's a very stable compound. Applying a thermodynamics lens isn't strictly accurate with workaround

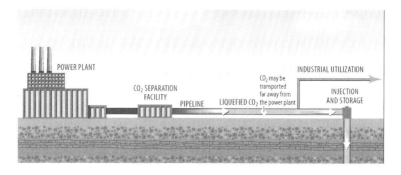

Figure 3.11 Carbon Capture.
Source: Used with permission from The NEED Project, www.NEED.org.

processes like adsorption, where you're trapping CO_2 rather than transforming it, but still serving the purpose of getting it out of the air. However, thermodynamics appears to hold the trump card. Professor Jen Wilcox, author of the book *Carbon Capture*, notes that with CCS, you need a great deal of energy.[47] Professor Wilcox also documents a current cost for CCS at \$120–\$140/ton,[48] comparable to the social cost of carbon used by TNC, if expensive compared to the current carbon offset market at \$15/ton. That doesn't mean the offset market is correct about actual project costs, but it is a large portion of what CCS is competing against if we're using market solutions.

Power plants generate a lot of waste energy as well as electricity, so they're good candidates for CCS. As of 2016, however, MIT had documented just 15 power plants where carbon capture was operative.[49] Lack of penetration into the power plant market is not necessarily a reason to not capture carbon, but it begs the question why. The answer: lack of economics to drive it. If there are no regulations requiring CCS, then there needs to be either enlightened voluntary effort or unenlightened allure of money to make it happen. The costs we just reviewed hinder the latter.

For those plants that do operate CCS, from a climate perspective, unfortunately, too much of the CO_2 product has been used for enhanced oil recovery.[50] So that's taking CO_2 out of the air, in order to extract more oil, combust it, and put CO_2 back into the air! That's not an argument to not pursue CCS, though, but rather an argument to find better uses. If you capture process CO_2 and make dry ice—as happens at ethanol plants—or use it for other industrial purposes, in many cases, eventually CO_2 just returns to the air. A useful byproduct is created, but not one that addresses our climate problem. One common proposal with CCS is for underground CO_2 injection, where the captured carbon is returned underground, ideally through the oil or gas well that brought it up in the first place. One issue is the potential for future generations to drill down and trigger a CO_2 bomb, even if CO_2 is a relatively dense gas and should tend to stay in the subsurface. That danger is just my speculation, however, and perhaps you're thinking I should look at research rather than spout opinion. I agree with you completely. And that's the problem. Who's tracking CO_2 leakage out of underground reservoirs? Even if oil companies were injecting CO_2 underground for enhanced oil recovery nearly 40 years ago, there's little track record of tracking leakage. Thus, you're stuck with my speculation. I've seen few others considering the issue, but among those who have, the Heinrich Böll Foundation is of similar mind.[51]

The more defensible approach is mineralizing CO_2; adding chemicals to convert it to limestone or a similar carbon-containing naturally occurring mineral to avoid gaseous escape, and achieve carbon removal that is more permanent than capturing carbon through reforestation or agricultural soils. Some start-ups are even producing cement with CO_2![52]

Direct air capture (DAC)

DAC is a variant of CCS, where you're working with ambient air concentrations of CO_2 rather than CO_2-rich exhaust gas on a smokestack. Ten years ago, MIT declared direct air capture had a prohibitively high price tag for CO_2 reduction.[53] Companies like Opus 12 are experimenting with DAC approaches, referring to it as "reverse combustion"[54] (and nature calls it photosynthesis!), but it still has high energy demand, and until that's renewably powered, it's not going to advance the climate cause. It's also a harder lift than CCS, as you are working with lower concentrations of CO_2 and you don't have available waste energy from a nearby power plant.

Enhanced mineral weathering

It turns out that rocks have sequestered trillions of tons of carbon dioxide over the eons. Silicate rocks are weathered by the low levels of mildly acidic CO_2 in water, and the CO_2 eventually gets trapped in carbonate compounds[55] (something like $Ca^{+2}(OH)_2 + CO_2 -> CaCO_3 + H_2O$). Calcium carbonate makes up coral reefs,[56] egg shells, and chalk, and is generally considered a fine compound to have around. There are ideas about how to enhance this process, finding the optimal type of rock and pulverizing it into powder to enhance carbon uptake. There are also concerns, like negative effects on soils where this pulverized powder is placed and alteration of ecosystems by rock extraction. Best bets are already disturbed sites like mining-affected areas, farmland, and tree plantations where there are already similar processes in place for fertilization and acidic soil management.[57]

There are other approaches to carbon removal, but those discussed represent key approaches.

Climatetech is attractive to many as an end-of-pipe solution that doesn't disrupt industries. Where tech options fit in-line with established industrial process and make real contributions, welcome. For example, ADM is capturing CO_2 off of a fermentation process and injecting it underground,[58] which has replication potential at breweries and other food processors. Please remember, though, that industrial sourcing of nonrenewable resources will eventually get disrupted, and if not eliminated, reincarnate in substantially different form, drawing from recycled or biobased feedstocks and powered by either clean energy or unclean energy where the uncleanliness is captured. Lay the groundwork now to make that transition easier and employ engineered carbon removal in parallel to tackle unavoidable climate impacts.

We need to see the signal-to-noise ratio improve with carbon removal technology. Better demonstration of technology is required to not only get results, but get to an acceptable price point (and at the risk of going broken record on you, a healthy price on carbon will shift that price point in climatetech's favor). The potential for land-based climatetech to disrupt ecosystems needs to be addressed where that is an issue, with climatetech best applied to altered/disturbed lands.

My crystal ball says we'll see some level of application of these technologies in this transition time of shifting from fossil fuels, in order to mitigate fossil fuel impacts while still using them. Which carbon removal technologies will be technically feasible and economically viable? That remains to be seen.

Drawdown returns

Project Drawdown was unveiled to great fanfare in 2017. Drawdown represents a multi-year effort involving over 100 researchers from around the globe to investigate the potential of 80+ technologies to "draw down" CO_2 levels in the atmosphere, if those technologies were implemented globally, through concerted effort, over the next 30 years.[59] I was honored to serve as one of those researchers.

Project Drawdown identifies a huge role for agriculture and the food industry supply chain. Eight of the top 20 global opportunities to reverse climate change fall into this sector. In addition to food, Drawdown articulates measures in energy (geothermal, wind, and solar), land use (reforestation, agriculture, and more), materials, transport, and buildings and cities.

In 2020, the Drawdown Review was released, restructuring recommendations around three themes:

- Reduce Sources
- Support Sinks
- Improve Society

On the face of it, that's pretty simple.

Reduce Sources = stop placing CO_2 and other GHGs in the air.
Support Sinks = do what you can to draw CO_2 out of the air.
Improve Society = find win-win options and multiple benefits in
    the process.

Your business climate strategy should embrace measures within these three themes. Reduce Sources is relatively well-worn ground, capturing the renewable energy, energy efficiency, and other measures to which we've given significant attention. Support Sinks tracks the carbon removal tactics we've just discussed, but let's look more closely via Table 3.1.

Drawdown organizes sinks into three categories of solutions, as shown in the table. These solutions will look quite similar to material we have reviewed. By their numbers, virtually all of the projected potential is in land solutions. It's striking that they don't see great potential for engineered solutions to remove carbon, but there's a reason for that. Drawdown is focusing on solutions that are available now, with CCS and other climatetech solutions placed in the arena of "coming attractions" that don't yet factor into the

Table 3.1 Drawdown Table

Category	Solutions (sub-solutions)	Potential (gigatons)
Land	Shift agriculture practices Protect and restore Ecosystems Use degraded land Address waste and diets	239–391
Coastal and ocean	Protect and restore coastal wetlands	1.1–1.5
Engineered	Biochar Coming attractions	2.2–4.4

Source: Author, created from Project Drawdown data.

bigger picture of drawing down the CO_2 levels in the air. Only biochar, a relatively understandable and established technology to more permanently capture woody carbon, is taken into account as an engineered solution.

Drawdown's perspective is independently consistent with my optimistic-if-cautionary notes on engineered solutions and climatetech. Drawdown takes a conservative stance for credibility, and awaits more evidence and proof-of-concept demonstrations before definitively claiming climatetech will play a large role. Before we put a lot of eggs into the engineered carbon removal implementation basket, eggs for more R&D are needed. A modest shift of our spending priorities will ensure plenty of eggs to go around. Engineered solutions are a fantastic arena for military investment, for example, given the climate crisis is our #1 national security threat according to the Pentagon.

One of the ten key insights lifted up by the review is:

Climate solutions are interconnected as a system, and we need all of them.

Improve Society as defined by Project Drawdown needs to happen as well as Reduce Sources and Support Sinks. One scenario is to place all your faith in engineered technologies, if in the longer term, to capture carbon at fossil fuel power plants and not change how we provide our energy. Though it's better than the non-capture alternative, assuming you navigate the problems we looked at earlier, technology can fail. And, ultimately, we need to think differently about how we provide our energy, incorporating the range of other solutions so technology failure won't break the emission allowances bank.

Another scenario is placing all your faith in natural and land-based sinks, expecting trees and agriculture to solve all the problems, and similarly not change business as usual. Regenerative agriculture is better than non-regenerative agriculture, but given the variability we just discussed, you're still not guaranteed to get the climate results you want.

The list of ten key insights also includes:

- *Climate solutions can have "co-benefits" that contribute to a better, more equitable world.*
- *The financial case for climate solutions is crystal clear, as savings significantly outweigh costs.*

The first insight hearkens back to the holistic value of natural solutions, where you get multiple benefits from a single climate action. For at least three decades, the environmental justice community has pointed out how time and again, burdens of pollution correlated with climate emissions fall on poor communities and communities of color. If you don't believe that, compare pollution in the most affluent areas of large metropolitan regions with pollution in the poorest areas in the same region. By reducing GHG emissions, we're often reducing co-pollutants that have direct toxic and health impacts, which lead to those co-benefits. And the co-benefits go beyond toxics to create whole new economies through climate investments, and create climate-friendly ventures that drive economic benefits as well as health benefits.

Though these insights from Drawdown are broader than simply the business community, the lessons apply. Use their findings to hone your big-picture strategy:

- Invest in a range of carbon sink solutions
- Commit to creating co-benefits through your climate actions

Notes

1 United Nations, "Special Climate Report: 1.5°C Is Possible But Requires Unprecedented and Urgent Action", United Nations, 2018. https://www.un.org/sustainabledevelopment/blog/2018/10/special-climate-report-1-5oc-is-possible-but-requires-unprecedented-and-urgent-action/

2 U.S. EPA, "Emissions & Generation Resource Integrated Database (eGRID)", U.S. EPA, 2020. https://www.epa.gov/energy/emissions-generation-resource-integrated-database-egrid

3 Matt Egan, "Secretive Energy Startup Backed By Bill Gates Achieves Solar Breakthrough", CNN Business, 2019. https://www.cnn.com/2019/11/19/business/heliogen-solar-energy-bill-gates/index.html

4 National Renewable Energy Laboratory, "PV Watts", Alliance for Sustainable Energy, LLC, https://pvwatts.nrel.gov/pvwatts.php

5 B.D. Hoen et al., United States Wind Turbine Database (ver. 3.3, January 14, 2021): U.S. Geological Survey, American Wind Energy Association, and Lawrence Berkeley National Laboratory. Map services and data are available from U.S. Wind Turbine Database. https://eerscmap.usgs.gov/uswtdb/

6 National Renewable Energy Laboratory (NREL), "2019 Annual Technology Baseline: Hydropower." NREL, Golden, CO, 2019. https://atb.nrel.gov/electricity/2019/index.html?t=hp

7 Dr. Babu Chalamala, "DOE OE Global Energy Storage Database", Sandia National Laboratories, 2020. https://www.sandia.gov/ess-ssl/global-energy-storage-database-home/

8 Steve Hanley, "It's Official—Consumer Reports Confirms EV Owners Spend Half as Much on Maintenance", CleanTechnica, September 26, 2020. https://cleantechnica.com/2020/09/26/its-official-consumer-reports-confirms-ev-owners-spend-half-as-much-on-maintenance/

9 U.S EPA, "GreenChill Partnership", U.S. EPA, 2020. https://www.epa.gov/greenchill

10 Whole Foods Market, "Environmental Stewardship: Our Green Mission", Whole Foods Market, 2020. https://www.wholefoodsmarket.com/mission-values/environmental-stewardship

11 Mushroom Packaging, "Custom Mycelium-Made Packaging", Ecovative Design, 2020. https://mushroompackaging.com/welcome

12 Mango Materials, "We Produce Materials for a Cleaner Future", Mango Materials, 2020. https://www.mangomaterials.com/products/

13 Full Cycle, "The Circular Revolution Is Here", Full Cycle, 2020. https://fullcyclebioplastics.com/

14 Department for Business, Energy & Industrial Strategy, "Greenhouse Gas Reporting: Conversion Factors 2019", Government of the United

Kingdom, 2020. https://www.gov.uk/government/publications/
greenhouse-gas-reporting-conversion-factors-2019

15 Center for Corporate Climate Leadership, "Emission Factors for Greenhouse Gas Inventories", U.S. EPA, March 26, 2020. https://www.epa.gov/sites/production/files/2020-04/documents/ghg-emission-factors-hub.pdf

16 North American Council for Freight Efficiency (NACFE), "Trailer Aerodynamics", NAFCE and RMI, 2020. https://nacfe.org/technology-guide/trailer-aerodynamics

17 United Airlines, "United Airlines Expands Industry-Leading Commitment to Biofuel, Powering More Flights with More Biofuel Than Any Other U.S. Carrier", United Airlines, May 22, 2019. https://hub.united.com/united-expands-commitment-biofuel-powering-flights-2637791857.html

18 Airbus, "Electric Flight", Airbus, 2021. https://www.airbus.com/innovation/zero-emission/electric-flight.html

19 Paul Horn, "Infographic: Why Farmers Are Ideally Positioned to Fight Climate Change", Inside Climate News, October 24, 2018. https://insideclimatenews.org/news/24092018/infographic-farm-soil-carbon-cycle-climate-change-solution-agriculture

20 Carbon Cycle Institute, "Carbon Farming", Carbon Cycle Institute. 2021. https://www.carboncycle.org/carbon-farming/

21 Fran Hoyle et al., "Labile Carbon", Soil Quality Pty Ltd, 2006. http://soilquality.org.au/factsheets/labile-carbon

22 Soil Carbon Initiative, "Soil Carbon Initiative", Green America, 2019. https://www.soilcarboninitiative.org/i

23 National Regenerative Agriculture Day, "National Regenerative Agriculture Day", What Would Love Do Now Ltd, 2021. https://www.nrad.org.au/

24 Jack Kittredge, "Soil Carbon Restoration: Can Biology Do the Job?", Northeast Organic Farming Association, Massachusetts Chapter, 2015. https://www.nofamass.org/soil-carbon-restoration-can-biology-do-the-job/

25 Colorado State University (CSU), "COMET-Farm", U.S. Department of Agriculture – NRCS and CSU, 2020. http://comet-farm.com/

26 Cool Farm Alliance (CFA), "Use the Cool Farm Tool", CFA, 2020. https://coolfarmtool.org/

27 Regenerative Rising, "Regenerative Earth Summit: Food + Fiber + Climate", Regenerative Rising, December 2018. https://regenerativerising.org/past-events/regenerative-earth-summit-food-fiber-climate-2018/#1485368436676-221b271a-cce1566f-129f

28 Center for Sustainability Solutions, "Soil & Climate Alliance", Green America, 2021. https://www.centerforsustainabilitysolutions.org/agriculture-network-index#agriculture-networks

29 #NoRegrets Initiative "#NoRegrets Initiative", Cienega Capital et al., 2020. https://www.noregretsinitiative.com/
30 Carbon Cycle Institute, "Carbon Farming", Carbon Cycle Institute. 2021. https://www.carboncycle.org/carbon-farming
31 Hannah Ritchie et al., "Environmental Impacts of Food", Our World in Data, January 2020. https://ourworldindata.org/environmental-impacts-of-food
32 Jared Geiser et al., "Dairy Cattle Impact on Beef Supplies", The Ohio State University, College of Food, Agricultural and Environmental Sciences, November 1, 2017. https://u.osu.edu/beef/2017/11/01/dairy-cattle-impact-on-beef-supplies/
33 Christopher Ketcham, "Allan Savory's Holistic Management Theory Falls Short on Science", Sierra Club, February 23, 2017. https://www.sierraclub.org/sierra/2017-2-march-april/feature/allan-savory-says-more-cows-land-will-reverse-climate-change
34 Jacob Williamson-Rea, "Want to Reduce Emissions? Start in the Gut of a Cow", Penn State University, October 26, 2018. https://penntoday.upenn.edu/news/limiting-amount-methane-produced-cattle
35 Tatiana Schlossberg, "An Unusual Snack for Cows, a Powerful Fix for Climate", Washington Post, November 27, 2020. https://www.washingtonpost.com/climate-solutions/2020/11/27/climate-solutions-seaweed-methane/?arc404=true
36 Paul Jun et al., "CH_4 and N_2O Emissions from Livestock Manure", Intergovernmental Panel on Climate Change, 2001. https://www.ipcc-nggip.iges.or.jp/public/gp/bgp/4_2_CH4_and_N2O_Livestock_Manure.pdf
37 Don Bugito, "Don Bugito: Prehispanic Snackeria", Don Bugito, 2020. https://www.donbugito.com/
38 Chirps, "Chirps", Chirps, 2020. https://eatchirps.com/
39 Sofia Khan et al., "Environmental Life Cycle Analysis: Impossible Burger 2.0", Impossible Foods, 2019. https://impossiblefoods.com/mission/lca-update-2019/
40 Justin Adams, "The Forgotten Climate Solution", The Nature Conservancy, February 17, 2016. https://www.nature.org/en-us/what-we-do/our-insights/perspectives/the-forgotten-climate-solution/
41 Pete Smith, Mercedes Bustamante et al., "Agriculture, Forestry and Other Land Use (AFOLU)", Intergovernmental Panel on Climate Change, 2014. https://www.ipcc.ch/site/assets/uploads/2018/02/ipcc_wg3_ar5_chapter11.pdf
42 The Nature Conservancy (TNC), "Nature's Make or Break Potential for Climate Change", TNC, October 16, 2017. https://www.nature.org/en-us/what-we-do/our-insights/perspectives/natures-make-or-break-potential-for-climate-change/
43 U.S. Forest Service (USFS), "Data and Decision Tools", USFS, December 23, 2016. https://www.fs.fed.us/research/urban/tools.php

44 U.S. Geological Service (USGS), "LandCarbon: Summary Results", USGS, April 21, 2017. https://www.usgs.gov/apps/landcarbon/tools/#

45 Matt Herbert, "New Greenhouse Gas Protocol Guidance on Carbon Removals and Land Use", World Resources Institute, October 15, 2019. https://ghgprotocol.org/blog/new-greenhouse-gas-protocol-standardsguidance-carbon-removals-and-land-use

46 Science Based Targets Network (SBTN), "Initial Guidance", SBTN, September 2020. https://sciencebasedtargetsnetwork.org/resources/guidance/

47 Presentation by Professor Jen Wilcox, Institute for Carbon Removal Law and Policy webinar, Earth Week 2020.

48 Ibid.

49 Massachusetts Institute of Technology, "Carbon Capture and Sequestration Technologies", MIT, September 30, 2016. http://sequestration.mit.edu/tools/projects/index_capture.html

50 Ibid.

51 Eva Mahnke, "Carbon Capture and Storage: Problems at Depth", Heinrich Böll Foundation, November 18, 2015. https://eu.boell.org/en/2015/11/18/carbon-capture-and-storage-problems-depth

52 David Biello, "Cement from CO2: A Concrete Cure for Global Warming?", Scientific American, August 7, 2008. https://www.scientificamerican.com/article/cement-from-carbon-dioxide/

53 Massachusetts Institute of Technology, "Carbon Capture and Sequestration Technologies", MIT, September 30, 2016. https://sequestration.mit.edu/research/aircapture.html

54 Opus 12, "We Have Developed a Device That Recycles CO2 into Chemicals and Fuels", Opus 12, 2020. https://www.opus-12.com/technology

55 Project Drawdown, Drawdown: The Most Comprehensive Plan Ever to Reverse Global Warming, "Coming Attractions", Project Drawdown, April 2017.

56 National Ocean Service, "What Is a Coral Reef Made of?", National Oceanic and Atmospheric Administration, December 4, 2020. https://oceanservice.noaa.gov/facts/coralmadeof.html

57 Project Drawdown, Drawdown: The Most Comprehensive Plan Ever to Reverse Global Warming, "Coming Attractions", Project Drawdown, April 2017.

58 Jessie Stolark, "ADM Deploys Carbon Capture and Sequestration Project at Illinois Ethanol Plant", Environmental and Energy Study Institute, April 13, 2017. https://www.eesi.org/articles/view/adm-deploys-carbon-capture-and-sequestration-project-at-illinois-ethanol-pl

59 Project Drawdown, "About Project Drawdown", Project Drawdown, 2017. http://www.drawdown.org

Chapter 4

Choose wisely

> No issue ranks higher than climate change on our clients' lists of priorities. They ask us about it nearly every day. . . .
>
> We know that climate risk is investment risk. But we also believe the climate transition presents a historic investment opportunity.
>
> – Larry Fink, BlackRock CEO

How you do something is as important as what you do, and how you do it will dictate the outcomes. In that light, differentiation between a good option and a bad option, or a good practice and a bad practice, is not always as clear as it might seem. How the practice is implemented affects your outcome.

Whether you're a business leader or other change agent, it's important to understand the nuances that make climate strategy execution successful.

Two specific areas where nuance affects how you implement:

- Carbon offsets. Once you've made what emissions reductions you can, the final action to address the footprint that remains is to invest in carbon offsets. Carbon offsets are purchases and projects to avoid or remove GHG outside of one's own operations. Some companies choose to offset their remaining emissions each year, whereas others will offset specific practices or products. Lyft, for example, had a program to purchase offsets for customer trips.[1] Even if they don't represent direct operational reductions, offsets can be part of a broader climate strategy, but in choosing them, there are a range of criteria to consider.

DOI: 10.4324/9781003191544-5

- Procurement options. Often in procurement we want to clearly have a better choice between two or more options. Although a better choice might be clear, having that clarity is not guaranteed, as we'll see. You can drill down into the specific aspects of the product you really care about (whether climate criteria or other), and employ tools like LCA to help you explore those aspects, but in any event, making a good choice requires some discernment.

Are carbon offsets good or bad?

> The problems caused by the mismatch between prices and values do not stem from a lack of skilled practitioners, but from a deep failure of the market to value our world properly.
> – Raj Patel

Carbon offsets are purchases and projects to avoid or remove GHG outside of one's own operations. Project types include:

- Renewable energy on someone else's buildings or lands
- Energy efficiency in someone else's buildings
- Super pollutant capture and destruction (usually methane or HFCs)
- Planting trees

You can buy offsets on retail sites (native.eco, b-e-f.org, goldstandard.org, etc.) as a business. Offsets are often used in lieu of making GHG reductions within one's own operations. For one, it is typically much cheaper to reduce a ton of emissions by buying offsets ($11–$15/ton on a recent scan of retail offset sites with tree planting, renewable energy, and other offset projects) than it is to implement a project yourself to do the same. For GHG reduction, I've seen $50–$500/ton for implementation costs, depending on the project. Tech company Stripe, in pursuing its Negative Emissions Commitment, reports prices of $75–$775/ton for carbon removal projects.[2]

This is where a flag has gone off for me many times in the past. If GHG reduction is that much more expensive in-house, how are offset market projects achieving GHG reductions so cheaply? With renewable energy offset projects, that situation is at least somewhat understandable, as the electricity itself is a salable product that helps finance the project, and the offset then just represents a portion of the implementation cost, not all. And reforestation projects might leverage existing tree planting programs, where you're just paying for another tree to be put into the system, and not paying the complete costs of distribution, planting, and maintenance to ensure survival. Short of providing a total exposé of offset financials, I want to at least help you be wary of very cheap offsets. If it seems too good to be true, it probably is, until your provider provides you a complete accounting of how they're delivering benefits for that price.

Offsets are often applied against those emissions where company staff feel that reductions aren't possible, whether unavoidable business travel or manufacturing processes that are currently locked into natural gas. Where companies are required by regulation to reduce emissions, some percentage of offsets is often allowed by the regulator for companies to achieve the regulated target. Regulating agencies like the California Air Resources Board typically have offset standards with associated offset project registries, like Verra and the American Carbon Registry, that act as clearinghouses of offset projects.

The question is to what extent offsets should play a role in your business climate strategy. Those who look will find a range of perspectives on whether carbon offsets are good or bad. Champions can't imagine how others can't see that their overseas forest restoration project is brilliant and badly needed, cost-effective, and carbon-effective. Opponents see the programs as an end run by polluters in prosperous countries to avoid reducing their impacts on local communities by funding reductions elsewhere.

Are these projects effective or ineffective? Enjoy the perennial cliché answer: it depends!

Although you could simply go to any number of retail registry sites to purchase what they deem relatively good, it's important to understand relevant criteria.

Several criteria should be investigated to judge project merits:

Locale: Where is the offset project based and what is the governance regime there?

Type: Does the project involve land-based trees, soil, renewable energy, energy efficiency, super pollutant destruction, or something else?

Rigor: Is the project verified or unverified, and if so, what level of verification?

Timeframe (critical, yet generally ignored!): How quickly will carbon be drawn out of the air to balance out the day or year of activity that put the carbon in the air? And when was the offset benefit created?

Free Will: Are GHG emission reductions mandated or voluntary? That is, is the entity required by law to drop their emissions, or just choosing to invest in offsets?

Thus far, I have somehow managed to avoid the wonky "additionality" and "leakage" terms frequently used when discussing offsets. In attempting to avoid those terms as best I can, they'll come up later.

Locale

Whether domestic or international, operating projects in areas with good governance is key. A project is best when designed and driven by the local community. Outside of that, locality still matters to an extent to support accountability. That doesn't mean longer-distance relationships can't work, but integrity all depends on the agreements and actions of the players involved (take that sentence out of context for wider applications).

One danger is incentivizing seizure of lands from current caretakers or indigenous peoples because potential financial returns have now been created through carbon credit markets, making it more attractive to seize the land. You could argue that pressure is always there as long as there are natural assets that could be converted into money, but the point is that we should be very intentional in offset project design and seek the best outcomes for all involved.

Project type

Where land use offset projects make a lot of sense: *restoring damaged and depleted lands* (notice a book theme here?). This includes coal mine methane capture, where mine has been abandoned and/ or under government or non-profit control; building soil carbon on farmlands that have been depleted of carbon; reforestation of deforested lands. We know what these lands were previously like. Restoring them is compatible with their recent ecological history and function. We have tens of millions of acres of depleted soils to work on in the United States alone. Capture and destruction of super pollutants from damaged areas—like methane leaks from animal feedlots, landfills, and abandoned coal mines—is important.

Where land-use offsets make less sense: *taking over undamaged lands.*

An area that has been a biodiverse, functioning ecosystem for decades could be negatively impacted by changing the habitat (e.g. adding trees to native prairie). If changing land management to increase carbon storage, that similarly holds potential to be unhealthy for the existing community of life on the land. Protect existing healthy land function and be wary of altering ecosystems solely for carbon benefit. We need to think holistically even when on the carbon quest.

Where land-use offsets make no sense: *incentives to damage ecosystems.*

I've seen too many solar projects (not funded by offset money as far as I know) that involve removal of many acres of trees. Let's strive to find better spaces to advance badly needed renewables, and leverage our already-built infrastructure, installing solar on buildings and around roadways. An option that's at least intellectually more interesting than never building solar in greenspace is to seek stacking functions, as the permaculturists say, and get multiple benefits in installation. An example is ground mount solar that incorporates pollinator habitat, as the company Clif Bar has highlighted.[3] There are multiple benefits in well-designed projects.

Renewable and efficiency projects can otherwise avoid some of the complications of land-based projects, in simply improving the performance of GHG-intensive equipment or constructing new renewable infrastructure on a relatively small footprint, where they have minimal other impacts (bird life, nuisance, noise, etc.). Projects like anaerobic digesters[4] can have multiple benefits: better odor control and byproduct generation that adds revenue.

Rigor

If it's not verified, then it's not verified. Quality of verification matters. Different programs might have different frequencies of re-verification to confirm that carbon benefits are being achieved over time. Whether you do offsets in or out of a strict verification/certification program and/or with a third party, benefits measurement and reporting should certainly happen.

Timeframe

If you produce a ton of emissions in a day—say through jet travel—and then as an offset, plant enough trees to take up a ton of emissions over 40 years, that's a problem if we need CO_2 levels significantly lower, like yesterday, and definitely lower in 10 years. Rates matter. It's not just magnitude.

I've seen little discussion about this in the offset industry, and am interested to hear how offset providers think about this issue, as it must come up. More importantly, it would be good to see what they can do to better match timeframe (e.g. the emissions of a given year are drawn back out the following year). Tree planting clearly has value. The solution could be to plant 40 times more trees to get the needed offset that year, and then apply future tree growth against your future emissions. If we don't do that, the atmosphere and oceans remain reservoirs in which CO_2 is increasing, as it is being drawn out of the air more slowly than it was emitted.

Free will

Too few distinguish between voluntary offsets and regulated offsets. That's a missed opportunity, in my humble opinion, to better resolve some entrenched differences between proponents and opponents.

Voluntary

It's hard to argue against companies voluntarily investing in renewables, reforestation, or other well-designed projects that create real benefits. Do your due diligence, and once you're sure any problems created by the project are relatively minimal, go for it. *And do not stop intelligently reducing your emissions in the process.* Serious companies are not slowing GHG reduction action—with its cost-saving, customer goodwill, public relations, and other benefits—simply because they wrote a check to grow trees or stockpile manure.

Regulated

The companies subject to GHG reduction regulations, such as high-volume emitters under California's cap-and-trade program, have quantified their emissions and need to reduce emissions. Let's assume regulations allow offsets against those emissions. We still have the *timeframe, additionality* (clarity that offset project would not have happened without offset funder money), *leakage* (avoided impacts at project site migrate elsewhere, like avoided deforestation on one plot of land simply driving deforestation to another plot of land, due to timber or beef demand), and other uncertainties of offset project success. Even when offsets are verified, complications can arise, like wildfires that make forest offset carbon literally go up in smoke. Programs can have reserves to mitigate that (e.g. require 30% more money to be invested to replace burned trees), but there will always be that risk with less permanent carbon storage like wood and even soils. That leads me to the position that those regulated entities, whether a country or Fortune 1000 company, should simply drop their emissions rather than complicate the scenario with a complex system of offsite offset project standards and tracking, that may or may not deliver CO_2 reductions in the necessary timeframe.

Particularly in affluent countries, we have the responsibility to tackle the problem that we're responsible for creating and which we continue to create. I'd really like overseas and offsite offset projects to work, as the financials are attractive and they hold the potential to improve lives overseas. There are ways to make those projects happen outside of regulated offsets, and I see too many complications in including them if our goal is credible emission reductions.

The offset provider industry still has a real role to play, though, in the regulatory scenario. Offset providers can support improvements within the regulated organizational boundary—on-site efficiency, on-site renewables, and R&D in emerging carbon removal solutions that hold some promise. Offset providers are particularly relevant when that boundary extends beyond your facilities to include your supply chain. Offset projects within your supply chain are now referred to as "insets" rather than offsets, to reflect how they exist within a boundary in which you have more control.

Regulators should certainly think about the implications of requiring drastic emission reductions on companies whose competitors may not be under the same regulation. However, that's more of an argument to me to soften the goal, if there's an actual hardship, rather than get into off-site/other country emissions, attempt to credit the benefit, and inject a lot more risk and uncertainty into that portion of the reduction.

If a regulated entity wanted to invest in GHG emission improvements in a peer entity under the same regulation, rather than invest in their own plant, that has merit and is not dissimilar from the inset concept. It's also reminiscent of the original cap-and-trade system that applied to sulfur pollution in the Ohio River valley. If the pool of total regulated emissions goes down, that serves the goal, ignoring the co-benefits of local reductions. Whether companies would be willing to invest in competitors is another matter, but where a range of industries are covered by the cap-and-trade program, there are non-competitive opportunities. When we reach outside the regulatory boundary to get credit offsets, that's where it's easy to get into trouble. Researchers at both UC Berkeley[5] and USC[6] documented that in-state emissions under California's cap-and-trade program actually increased, due to offsets and a decrease in out-of-state imports. If allowing investments at other regulated facilities, note that allowance won't meet all the concerns of the environmental justice and climate justice communities, and you still have valid reasons to keep those GHG reductions local, but if you're laser-focused on carbon and willing to give up the co-benefits, you can make an argument for that type of offset.

Resources

The GHG Management Institute and the Stockholm Environmental Initiative offer a Carbon Offset Guide to help you secure high-quality offsets as well as help avoid low-quality offsets.[7] GreenBiz provides a more recent overview of offsets to explain and explore the concepts above, if also noting that trying to understand carbon offsets is "like stepping into quicksand"[8] and the market-place is still "a wild west."[9] Watch your step and watch your back! You can find respected offset providers who care about meaningful projects if you look.

We may never see consensus around offsets, but real dialogue around their benefits and shortcomings, among a range of perspectives, is important.

Is product **X** better or worse than product **Y**?

> [The European Central Bank] has to look at all the business lines and the operations in which we are engaged in order to tackle climate change, because at the end of the day, money talks.
> – Christine Lagarde, Head of the European Central Bank

A dilemma that continually presents itself is which of two or more purchasing options is the better choice. A common tool through which businesses make that evaluation is life cycle assessment (LCA). To recap, LCA is a process of looking at all the inputs throughout your supply chain and calculating all the outputs from input processing: byproducts, emissions, and other releases to air, land, and water. Those outputs typically get distilled into a handful of indicators: resource depletion, GHG emissions, and the effects on air, land, and water that stem from those releases. When applying LCA in a consistent way on two product options, you can compare product indicators to judge whether one is better or worse.

As much as I hold up LCA as a powerful tool for decision-making, the truth is that the results are highly dependent on your assumptions and your choices of analytical boundaries. That's a dense truth with which to grapple. That doesn't mean there isn't value in taking a rigorous LCA approach to compare alternatives, but you do need to be clear about those choices and their implications for LCA results.

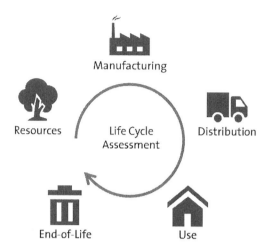

Figure 4.1 LCA Diagram.
Source: GreenDelta GmbH.

Arenas of LCA choice include:

* Boundaries
* "Functional unit"
* "Allocation"

Boundaries

The boundaries of your owned facilities are quite clear. The boundaries of your supply chain are less clear, in that when you extend upstream to Tier 1, 2, and 3 suppliers, your direct Tier 1 relationships are known, but who those suppliers source from (Tier 2 and beyond) isn't necessarily clear. To understand total impact, you should also think downstream through distribution, customer use, and disposal. With LCA, the boundary choice you have is how far along the upstream-downstream chain to take your analytics. You can look at impacts from sourcing through manufacturing (called cradle-to-gate), sourcing through customer use to end of life (cradle-to-grave), or, if you're really cool, sourcing through customer use to recapture of your product for reuse (cradle-to-cradle).

Different boundary choices will give you different results. At least as important, you get different information by which to make decisions. There's not a lot of fame in LCA, but one relatively well-known study by Levi Strauss & Co found a large portion of the life cycle energy impact of jeans was in the washing of jeans by customers. They would not have discovered that if simply conducting a cradle-to-gate assessment.

Functional unit

Functional unit is the amount of product or service that you're going to use to compare two or more alternatives. Functional unit demands that you make sure you're comparing the same level of service provided between different product options. With LCA, we actually can compare apples to oranges, EVs with combustion engine vehicles, and a great many other things with their alternatives, if you get the functional unit right. In the Levi's example, it's tempting to use a pair of jeans as the unit of comparison. However, if a pair of Levi's lasts 10 years, and the alternative lasts five years, that's not a fair comparison. Durability needs to be considered, so in this case, you could look at ten years equivalent of clothing, meaning two of the alternatives equal one pair of Levi's and you then run your LCA accordingly. In comparing different cleaning products, like sprays versus wipes, the functional unit could be 100 sq. ft. of cleaned surface, where you then determine how many wipes and how much spray would be needed to provide that level of service. Any good choice for functional unit should ensure equity, but there's certainly potential for error.

Allocation

Another example of choice in the field of life cycle analysis is "allocation." In manufacturing, you might have a line that generates several products—call them by-products or co-products—and you then have different choices around allocating the impacts of the manufacturing process to different co-products. For example, production of corn ethanol generates ethanol, corn solids that can be used in feed, and CO_2 that can be captured and used in applications like dry ice.[10] Anaerobic digesters take organic waste and can produce biogas, electricity (if biogas is combusted on-site), and undigested fiber for animal bedding.[11] Some organizations will allocate on a mass basis. If ethanol is 50% of the outgoing product by mass, then it is credited with 50% of the climate, air, and water impacts of the process. Others may choose to allocate on a value basis; if ethanol is only 30% of the revenue, then it is credited with 30% of impacts. You can make arguments either way, and get different results. Since most businesses stay in business based on revenues, I'd often argue for value allocation. Where a process is not driven by revenue, allocation by mass basis often tracks the physical reality of matter and energy.

There's real potential for product X to be better or worse than product Y, depending on choices of boundaries and the approach to allocation. And that's not even starting the conversation around which indicator you're looking at. LCA typically looks at several indicators as mentioned earlier which may include:

- GHG emissions
- Toxicity indicators
- Mineral and biobased resource use
- Other air and water emissions

Product X could be better on some indicators and not others, as depicted in Figure 4.2, even before you look at changing your assumptions.

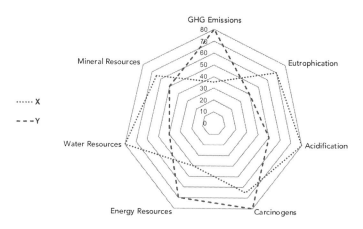

Figure 4.2 Products X and Y.
Source: Author.

Before throwing up your hands, saying nothing matters, and otherwise falling into moral relativism, let me be clear that you still need to seek to get the clearest understanding of impacts that you can. Analysis and analytical tools remain crucially important. However, you do need to be careful with your assumptions and aware of your options. Choices matter. The point is to have enough rigor for defensible results. One way to improve awareness is through sensitivity analysis, where you adjust assumptions and choices, and see how significantly those assumptions and choices change the results. I wholeheartedly recommend you experiment with sensitivity analysis to make sure you are comfortable with your chosen direction and not making decisions solely based on a very sensitive and uncertain factor.

The entire purpose of this effort, whether through LCA or an alternative approach, is to guide you to the best choices, whether you're comparing two different product alternatives, or you're comparing the relative contributions of different life cycle stages of one product, evaluating raw material, material processing, packaging and distribution impacts to identify where to place your improvement efforts.

In determining where to improve, it's also important to think about your level of control. Returning to the Levi's example, Levi's doesn't directly control how users are washing jeans. They can use influence, attempt to reach consumers to raise awareness, encourage use of cutting-edge technology like the clothesline, and work with washing and drying machine manufacturers on efficiency. However, they ultimately don't have direct control. There's still value in looking within their own facility boundaries where they do have direct control to determine where they'll get the biggest impact for their investments in GHG and water reduction. Levi's staff have in fact explored a laser-driven process to "stonewash" jeans, avoiding great amounts of bleaching agent, reducing processing time, and getting jeans to the customer faster.[12] You, too, must find ways within and without your operations to reduce product impacts.

Notes

1 Matt McFarland, "Lyft Cuts Carbon Offsets, Promises to Transition to Electric Vehicles by 2030", CNN, June 17, 2020. https://edition.cnn.com/2020/06/17/tech/lyft-electric-cars/index.html

2 Ryan Orbuch, "Stripe's First Carbon Removal Purchases", Stripe, May 18, 2020. https://stripe.com/blog/first-negative-emissions-purchases

3 Clif Bar, "Clif Bar & Company Makes Leading Investment in Renewable Energy", Clif Bar, September 24, 2019. https://www.clifbar.com/press-releases/clif-bar-company-makes-leading-investment-in-renewable-energy

4 U.S. EPA, "How Does Anaerobic Digestion Work?", U.S. EPA, January 22, 2021. https://www.epa.gov/agstar/how-does-anaerobic-digestion-work

5 Robert Sanders, "California's Cap-and-Trade Air Quality Benefits Go Mostly Out of State", University of California, Berkeley, July 10, 2018. https://news.berkeley.edu/2018/07/10/californias-cap-and-trade-air-quality-benefits-go-mostly-out-of-state/

6 Lara Cushing et al., "A Preliminary Environmental Equity Assessment of California's Cap-and-Trade Program", USC Equity Research Institute, September 14, 2016. https://dornsife.usc.edu/PERE/enviro-equity-CA-cap-trade

7 Carbon Offset Guide, "What Makes a High-Quality Carbon Offset?", GHG Management Institute and the Stockholm Environment Institute, 2021. http://www.offsetguide.org/high-quality-offsets/

8 Jesse Klein, "In the Quest for Carbon Offsets, (Almost) Anything Goes", GreenBiz Group, November 30, 2020. https://www.greenbiz.com/article/quest-carbon-offsets-almost-anything-goes

9 Heather Clancy and Joel Makower, GreenBiz 350 Podcast, GreenBiz Group, December 4, 2020. https://www.greenbiz.com/article/episode-247-biden-wish-lists-supporting-intersectional-environmentalists

10 Alto Ingredients, "Distiller Proteins", Alto Ingredients, Inc., 2021. https://www.pacificethanol.com/co-products

11 David Jaber, Unpublished Methane Digester Research, David Jaber, 2015.

12 Michael Kobori, Presentation at Peterson Forum by Levi Strauss & Co's VP of Sustainability, UC Berkeley Haas School of Business, September 2019.

Chapter 5

Seek the truth and it shall set you free

> We have to wake up to the fierce urgency of the now.
> – Jim Yong Kim, World Bank president,
> on the climate crisis

An aspect of business that is relevant to climate—and extends well beyond it—is integrity. Ruin your reputation by misrepresentation on one issue, and stakeholders will start to distrust your climate strategy and performance claims, too. Truthtelling, in alignment with your best understanding of the facts, is important.

Areas where truth particularly matters in connection with climate include:

* Clarity on definitions of terms
* Product carbon footprint claims

Don't believe the hype

Public Enemy was onto something over 30 years ago.[1]

"We do regenerative agriculture."
"We have a circular product."
"We are a climate-friendly company."
What do all these claims have in common?

DOI: 10.4324/9781003191544-6

Figure 5.1 Public Enemy.
Source: Author's copyright-compliant image.

At minimum, they are claims that need to be tested. They may have a certain "truthiness," to quote Stephen Colbert, but without a standard to test against—that is, a definition of "regenerative," "circular," and "climate-friendly"—they're effectively meaningless. Until those definitions are in place, you can't believe the hype. It's like labeling your product "Locally Made" and having no idea where your product is being sent.

Many companies have enough sustainability sophistication to avoid making ungrounded statements, and they get there by employing a critical mass of staff and/or consultants who know enough to avoid the trap. In the 2020 State of the Profession report, GreenBiz documents how sustainability staffing for a large fraction of companies has consistently increased since 2014.[2] In an evolving world with new issues and new terms, it's understandable that a company might get caught. You will get caught unless you invest in scanning emerging trends and deeply understanding them.

Reasons a company might make statements like those above fall into a few camps.

Not knowing what you don't know

Many companies committing the error of effectively meaningless statements do so because they're not monitoring the issue at hand and literally don't know what they don't know. The Dunning-Kruger effect from psychology illustrates how the ignorant often think they're knowledgeable, and that's not a position you want your business to be in, publicly or privately.[3] The dated example that's become rare, but is still alive: thinking "we recycle, therefore we're sustainable" and not interrogating any further.

You can mangle what you don't measure

Closely related to not knowing what you don't know is to understand the issue at hand and have awareness of what you should verify to make the claim, but you simply do not verify. Verification might require measurement. Through the act of measuring, you know whether or not you're mangling, and you know whether or not you're hitting the threshold of what's required to make a claim.

Deliberate deception

This is pretty self-explanatory. Deception is often not visible from the outside, but you can find examples (Volkswagen emissions testing, for example). It's hard to do this with serious matters and be able to sleep at night without somehow justifying your actions to yourself. Possibly the greatest related sin that enables deception is to think the claim is inconsequential, and subsequently think it does not matter what you claim. That is, you do not realize that the terms you use have weight. Companies that engage in deceptive claims could be creating enough positive impact to have some truthiness to the claims they make, but those with decision-making power are just not curious enough to seek more truth.

The thresholds under which one can make a claim aren't always clear. Many claims are defined by a regulation or a certification standard, like LEED helping define whether or not you have a green building. For the circular product and climate-friendly claims offered as examples earlier, there isn't yet a broadly accepted standard that has been set. That's when it's particularly important to not get ahead of yourself and not make claims for which you have no basis. "Net zero" is a good example which we'll dive into in a few pages. Though it essentially means the same as "carbon neutral," because there is significant effort underway to better define how you achieve net zero, I advise you to not claim you've achieved net zero until that's settled.

The above may read as a call for certification, though that's not my real intent. Certification is certainly a tool we keep applying to problems, correlated with the rise and proliferation of the eco-label as a means to convey that not all claims are hype. When we come up with a standard, and want companies to follow the standard, certification comes into play for an added level of rigor that lends validity to the standard. Options are determined by the group managing the certification, and could include the following:

- Self-certification. Self-certification eases the effort required and avoids the bureaucracy of certification. However, it means nothing without transparency, so others can at least check how certification is done. Else, you have a conflict of interest in wanting the certification, and there is no way without transparency for anyone else to verify whether you actually met the standard.
- Third-party certification. Third party helps to eliminate the conflict of interest within self-certification and, if adding bureaucracy, it helps ensure rigor. Conflict of interest has a way of returning, though. For example, if the client is paying the certifier to do the certification, conflict of interest could just migrate over to the certifier, who in theory could lose a renewed contract if their client doesn't get a passing grade. One approach to help eliminate that is to have yet another body to certify the certifier and otherwise audit the work.

If you seek many different certifications and are successful, your products start to look more like NASCAR contestants than customer choices, blanketed with ecolabels. Behind the ecolabel barrage is a litany of certification effort, if there's any rigor to the certification. The level of effort required then becomes its own project. Innovative ways to cut through the effort might include applying tools like blockchain (if yet another tool on which to not believe the hype until there are demonstrated examples) to verifiably track transactions throughout the value chain. To what extent that transparency makes certification data management more manageable remains to be seen, and I don't claim to have any particular insights into the back-end information management of most ecolabels.

If not necessarily involving certification, the solution to avoiding problematic claims should definitely involve standards and common definitions, whenever a term rises to the level of having market cache and real market value. At the end of the day, you need to navigate use of terms and tools with integrity. This will help your businesses avoid untrue claims, and help ensure your products live up to their hype.

One minus one doesn't equal zero

When is zero carbon footprint not zero carbon footprint? This may look like the start of a joke at climate nerd happy hour. However, it relates to an actual question that arose on a project where the client company was seeking to claim their product had zero carbon footprint. It is a not-so-ancient riddle that demands less truthiness and yet more truth-seeking.

Let's start with some definitions and their caveats:

- Net zero. The GHG emissions from a building, a product supply chain, or an organization are offset by reducing an equivalent amount of GHG from outside the boundaries of that building, product, or organization. This could be achieved by installing enough renewables onsite to where you're selling as much energy to the grid as you're pulling from it. My caveat is that there are programs working on more formal definitions for achieving net zero as an organization, as detailed below.
- Zero carbon. No GHG emissions involved in creating product. Zero is different than net zero.
- Carbon neutral/climate neutral. Equivalent to net zero as described above. You create some emissions in your operations and you avoid an equal amount of emissions within or without your operations.
- Carbon negative. Going beyond net zero/carbon neutral to remove even more emissions than is generated in the process. The net effect of product creation and/or company operations is that GHG in the atmosphere is reduced on a CO2-equivalent basis.
- Climate positive! There is a strong movement among climate action advocates seeking to reframe what we're doing as positive. Rather than think about less bad, with a goal of zero impact, we think about the net benefit of pulling GHG out

of the air, into soil, products, or other. I rebranded my firm to Climate Positive Consulting to better capture that notion, and the rebrand has helped more clearly communicate what I do to sustainability directors and other decision-makers at least peripherally aware of these terms. Climate positive equals carbon negative, but please don't tell any positivists that I told you that!

Clearly, there's a morass of terms. Terry Nguyen of Vox chronicled related product claims: a "climate positive" parka and burger, a "carbon negative" vodka, a "carbon neutral" shipping service, a "carbon zero" commuting app, and "zero carbon" coffee.[4] Clearly, the term business is booming! The net zero business itself is booming. BusinessGreen contributors James Murray and Tom Gockelen-Koslowski have documented that the number of businesses with net zero commitments more than tripled over 2020.[5]

Let's also make sure we distinguish between a net zero/carbon neutral *organization* and a net zero/carbon neutral *product.* Generally, the former should deliver the latter. Companies that are not net zero/carbon neutral as an organization may invest to declare a specific product line net zero. For example, they could purchase offsets specifically for the purpose of offsetting the product footprint.

How you assess whether you're net zero, carbon negative, or nowhere near those benchmarks is through the GHG Protocol and the GHG accounting process detailed in Chapter 2. If you go through that accounting process and only come up with a number, the story you can tell is not compelling. "Yes, our product has climate impacts that we wish it didn't." The number needs to be tied to a strategy for footprint reduction, even if the strategy is more modest than carbon neutral/net zero. As companies have amped up their responsibility efforts, renewables have gotten impressively cheaper, and, notwithstanding earlier caveats, offset markets have been recognized to allow reduction and removal of carbon from places outside of company boundaries. We have arrived at a place where there's potential to claim net zero carbon organizations and product lines.

With definitions out of the way, fast forward to the project dilemma. A start-up client was using renewable energy to create its product, and the feedstock involved capturing GHGs that would have otherwise escaped into the atmosphere, incorporating them into the product. The resulting product was credibly zero carbon by the definition above, and the client wanted to claim that they had a zero carbon product. Fine. Their production process was well designed for avoiding GHG emissions. Several months passed. The feedstock source gets disrupted. Client has to use traditional feedstock with an associated GHG footprint and invests in offset projects elsewhere. Is the product itself still zero carbon?

My answer was "no." Choosing to offset emissions outside of the process is different than choosing a process that inherently reduces emissions. You can claim you're offsetting the footprint, and reach for a net zero claim, but not that the footprint itself is zero. Even if the post-disruption product in this client example is still quite elegant compared with business as usual, the physical reality of what happens matters. The PAS 2050 and ISO 14067 product carbon footprint standards agree with me that offsets should not be used in reporting carbon footprint.

This may seem like nitpicking, but it serves a purpose. "Net zero" carbon emissions is the term that's gained traction rather than "zero carbon" emissions for a reason. Net zero allows for emissions with offsets that are then applied. Zero carbon does not allow for emissions. The start-up client was exceptional in that zero carbon is too far away from virtually everyone else's reality, unless you're a tree (and then you get to also claim carbon negative!). You can theoretically have elegant manufacturing processes that involve no GHG emissions in their supply chain, but it remains exceedingly rare for the moment. In his book, *The Value of Nothing*, Raj Patel explores how markets place value on some items that are worth nothing, and how markets don't value other items that are priceless,[6] popularizing the value of nothing. I'm popularizing the value of zero.

Net zero in an age that remains dominated by fossil fuel use is a notable accomplishment. If you achieve it, more power to you, but be careful about language. What's worse than not being able to make a claim is to have a PR nightmare because your claims get ahead of your reality.

In seeking product standards, the product life cycle accounting standard offered by the GHG Protocol explicitly states that "This standard is . . . not designed to be used for quantifying GHG reductions from offsets or claims of carbon neutrality."[7] That might feel like ducking the carbon neutral question for those of us seeking answers from *the* GHG protocol people, but given the nuances of carbon neutral versus net zero versus zero emissions, you can see why they defer. And even though I offered a definition of net zero above, there's not yet consensus on definitions and pathways—as consulting firms Quantis[8] and 3Degrees[9] have also affirmed. The Science Based Targets Initiative (SBTi) is working to help define net zero organizations, recognizing there is not currently a global standard.[10] Over one quarter of the B Corporation community has committed to net zero by 2030, with a great start at offering a net zero definition, though whether those B Corporations will be required to hit specific reduction thresholds remains to be seen. Because of the level of definition activity that is underway as of 2021, I would not run ahead yet with making net zero organizational claims, and encourage you to consult SBTi and B Corporation Climate Collective websites as you move forward to gauge when definitions have been settled.

For products, others have put thought into product footprints, taking the concepts of carbon neutral and net zero and defining how those could apply to your product. Beyond the product carbon footprint standards mentioned earlier (PAS 2050, ISO 14067, GHG Protocol) to crunch the numbers, there are also certifications to distinguish your product once the numbers are crunched. Organizations involved with those definitions and certifications include the following.

Living Product Challenge (LPC)

Created by the International Living Future Institute, LPC has requirements for seven different aspects of products (Water, Energy, Materials, etc.) with 20 imperatives among those areas. All 20 imperatives as shown in Table 5.1 need to be met for full certification, with a handful of imperatives in bold required for any partial levels of certification.

Table 5.1 Living Product Challenge

Petal	Imperative
Place	**Responsible place** Habitat exchange Living economy sourcing
Water	**Water footprint** Net positive water
Energy	**Energy footprint** Net positive energy
Health and happiness	**Red list** Transparent material health Human thriving
Materials	**Responsible industry** Regenerative materials Net positive waste Net positive carbon
Equity	**Ethical supply chain** Equitable investment Just organizations Social co-benefits
Beauty	**Inspiration + education** Beauty + spirit

Source: Author, adapted from International Living Future Institute, Living Product Challenge v2.0.

LPC does not explicitly require climate neutrality or net zero carbon. It does require the similar "net positive energy," requiring the product manufacturer to generate at least as much energy as is used to create the product, through efficiency and renewable energy throughout the supply chain.[11]

Climate Neutral Certified

Climate Neutral offers a Measure->Offset->Reduce->Label process, offering their own calculator to generate your product footprint, a reduction plan template to reduce those emissions, and link to offset providers from which to procure offsets to address that footprint.[12] An emissions reduction plan is required, though neutrality can lean heavily on the offset portion.

Carbon Neutral protocol

Carbon Neutral, developed by Natural Capital Partners, refers users to the GHG Protocol. Carbon Neutral offers five steps to get to carbon neutral, each with requirements and guidance. Carbon Neutral is quite similar to Climate Neutral, in that though it encourages emission reductions, it is also through offsets that neutrality is delivered.[13]

The Science Based Targets Initiative does not allow offsets due to concerns that we need to be making emissions reductions directly in our operations and supply chains. In that spirit, Living Product Challenge comes closest to the SBT intent, as it's asking for the energy generation to happen *within* the supply chain, where Climate Neutral and Carbon Neutral allow offsets that can be distant from your value chain. "Insets" within your supply chain rather than offsets elsewhere is where we see the field going, as the carbon benefit is directly tied to your business. To their credit, both Climate Neutral and Carbon Neutral encourage SBTs to ensure serious reductions. There has been market energy shifting toward Climate Neutral, and it is a certification to have on your radar.

The tasks for businesses that are serious in tackling product footprint are given as follows:

•   Keep watching these terms and their evolution. There will be implications for organizational claims as well as product claims.
•   Consider net zero, as the term that is gaining real market traction. In setting on the net zero/carbon neutral/carbon negative/climate positive path, with 1,500+ other companies on their way, you are in good company.

Notes

1 "Don't Believe the Hype", Public Enemy. Track off of the "It Takes a Nation of Millions to Hold Us Back" Album, 1988. https://www.youtube.com/watch?v=LK8sxngSWaU
2 John Davies, "State of the Profession", GreenBiz Group, April 2020.

3 Psychology Today, "Dunning-Kruger Effect", Psychology To-day, 2021. https://www.psychologytoday.com/us/basics/dunning-kruger-effect
4 Terry Nguyen, "More Companies Want to Be "Carbon Neutral." What Does That Mean?", Vox, June 16, 2020. https://www.vox.com/the-goods/2020/3/5/21155020/companies-carbon-neutral-climate-positive
5 James Murray and Tom Gockelen-Koslowski, "Global Net-Zero Commitments Double in Less than a Year", GreenBiz Group, September 23, 2020. https://www.greenbiz.com/article/global-net-zero-commitments-double-less-year
6 Raj Patel, The Value of Nothing, Raj Patel, 2009. http://rajpatel.org/2009/10/27/the-value-of-nothing/
7 GHG Protocol, Product Life Cycle Accounting and Reporting Standard, World Resources Institute and World Business Council for Sustainable Development, 2013. https://ghgprotocol.org/product-standard
8 Alexi Ernstoff, "Reductions or Removals? Why Science—Not Just Market Forces—Must Shape Our Pathway to Net Zero", Quantis, August 10, 2020. https://quantis-intl.com/why-science-not-market-forces-must-shape-our-pathway-to-net-zero/
9 3Degrees, "Pathways to Net Zero Emissions" Webinar, 3Degrees, May 26, 2020.
10 Science Based Targets Initiative, "Net-Zero", Science Based Targets Initiative, 2021. https://sciencebasedtargets.org/net-zero/
11 International Living Future Institute, Living Product Challenge 2.0, International Living Future Institute, 2019.
12 Climate Neutral, "How It Works", Climate Neutral, 2020. https://www.climateneutral.org/how-it-works
13 Carbon Neutral, "Requirements", Natural Capital Partners, 2021. https://www.carbonneutral.com/the-carbonneutral-protocol/5-steps-to-achieving-carbonneutral-certification/step-4-reduce

Chapter 6

Consider more than carbon

A future without climate change . . . is no longer possible. But a beautiful future is still ours if we are willing to struggle for it.
– Gus Speth, dean emeritus, Yale School of the Environment

We've discussed how to measure emissions, how to quantify footprint, emission reduction project types, how to prioritize projects, and how to gauge the quality of carbon removal projects. We've also looked at potential pitfalls, both in projects themselves and in communication claims about those climate projects.

To help complete the picture, let's visit a handful of carbon footprint-adjacent topics that ideally influence the decisions you make around your products and facilities. These topics are important enough that they should be weighed along with any decisions you make to advance your climate strategy, particularly where there seem to be trade-offs. Those topics are both internal and external to your company and include:

Internal
- Business model
- Business climate risk

External
- Biodiversity
- Government policy

DOI: 10.4324/9781003191544-7

Business model: too big to not fail?

> Capitalism, as we know it, is dead.
>   – Marc Benioff, Salesforce CEO

It's a good time to pause and take stock from a big-picture view.

We've collectively made progress over 20 years toward the SDG sustainability vision. Yet, at least three of the nine planetary limit trends we reviewed earlier are alarming, including the primary trend we care about here—the march of CO_2 levels ever upward. Why haven't we made more progress toward the vision? Why are those planetary limit trends where they are? All the concerted climate activity that we're compelled to tackle encourages us to revisit how we landed in the situation of climate crisis in the first place. There are structural reasons we get locked into continuing the climate errors of the past.

One clear culprit in the continuation of our climate crisis is in how we manage commerce. Economic activity that (1) is predicated on fossil fuels and pollution, and (2) has built-in incentives to always grow larger is clearly problematic. Together, those two drivers are a beast. That's presenting the issue at the macro-level, but you see the same pattern at the micro-level in individual businesses. In so many organizations, there's an inherent drive to grow: for market share, for leverage over suppliers, for fear of competitors taking the same growth actions and driving down revenue. Where businesses on this treadmill have a large carbon footprint, the climate crisis is exacerbated. Thus, you have business leaders like Marc Benioff, who've been enormously successful in this system of commerce, nevertheless calling out what are clearly problems.

For too many stakeholders, business is a bad word, even if business generates wealth for their communities and creates the products they use. That's not only due to climate impacts, of course. Both negative climate trends and negative public opinion are related to many negative impacts that stem from scaling and concentration of power—moving factories overseas, seeking lowest cost labor and fewer regulatory restrictions. Many of us would like to make business more consistently a good word, but the opposing view is impossible to dispel while there are negative impacts at large scale.

Let's return to those two factors working in tandem:

Driver 1: Economy based on fossil fuel and depletion of nature.
Driver 2: Incentives to grow the economy ever larger.

Eliminate Driver 1, and growing companies large and small are no longer escalating their GHG emissions. Scaling the number and size of companies is no longer a climate issue. Eliminate Driver 2, and there are still GHG emissions, but they are bounded by the type of steady-state economy now endorsed by many environmental economists. Think of it as economic activity operating within the doughnut of Doughnut Economics which, as shown in Figure 6.1, provides a social foundation to meet human needs without stressing ecological limits.[1]

One pathway to reverse Driver 1 is to have our utilities shift toward all renewable electricity, and transition away from fossil-sourced natural gas, without other action required by other businesses (except electrification of some fuel-based processes). Another pathway, and not one that is mutually exclusive, is through corporate commitment, where businesses choose to do the transition themselves—electrifying processes and installing renewables. The intent of this book is to help you do precisely that. Reversing Driver 1 needs to happen and is happening.

With Driver 1 reversed, Driver 2 is less of an issue, but simply switching over utilities doesn't address the non-energy GHG impacts in your supply chain. The impacts of growth and scaling remain issues beyond GHG emissions, given all the water, materials, community infrastructure and other resources required to power the economy, unless you improve the use efficiency of all those resources in parallel, and ensure good relationships with the communities into which you're expanding. Scaling pressures notwithstanding, for a given product or service, there's typically only so much market available. Shifting customer perspectives and advertising efforts to boost consumption can increase or decrease market size, dramatically at times, and it's also possible to

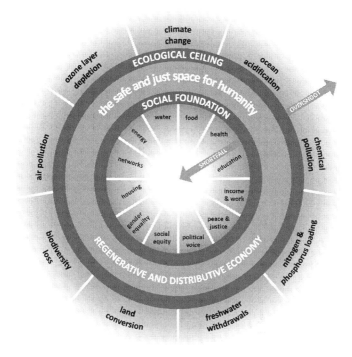

Figure 6.1 Doughnut Economics.
Source: Doughnut Economics Action Lab.

erroneously invest resources in overproduction, but market size at a given point in time generally provides some bound on the activity. Individual businesses might acquire other competitors or offer new products in their own scaling, but that doesn't grow the market for the initial product.

What is certainly an issue is how we ensure climate remains a business priority, whatever our scale. What energy sources are you drawing on to power facilities and your supply chain? In land use, are you engaged in greenfield development in an environmentally sensitive area, or developing already degraded areas? What land use practices are used by the suppliers from which you source? The goal should be to generate as much revenue as possible per ton of

GHG emissions, irrespective of business scale, and deliver prosperity with a lower climate price tag.

Increases in emissions can happen in multiple ways: increasing numbers of companies, increasing size of companies, drops in fossil fuel use efficiency, or degradation of nature leading to lower natural capacity to remove emissions. It is the scaling of GHG generation that is more important than the numbers and sizes of individual companies. That said, CDP, as *the* business-friendly forum for voluntary international business climate reporting, and not exactly an anti-corporate climate justice group, pointed out only 100 companies are responsible for 70+% of global emissions.[2] That's a striking statistic. If climate action had been a priority earlier in the business lives of CDP's top 100 emitters, it's quite possible those businesses would not be in the top 100. You can certainly argue that the drive to scale can compete with other priorities like keeping GHG footprint in check. However, increasing GHG among 100,000 companies rather than 100 isn't a climate solution.

The way we'll overcome the increase of GHG is through an all-of-the-above policy approach:

- Decarbonize utilities (generally on a government level)
- Decarbonize our business facilities, vehicles, and systems
- Ensure natural resources are regenerated after their use, and find ways for consumption to avoid natural resource degeneration in the first place
- Curtail the linear economy

Do I think properly attuned companies, regardless of scale, will invest very significant resources into ensuring they don't fail at achieving bold climate goals, find ways to do business that are compatible with GHG-free futures, and decouple profit from pollution? It's not an issue of what I think. Actions of the properly attuned are happening as you read this. The existence of this book is a reflection of that fact, and a reflection of the seriousness with which businesses are embedding climate action into operations.

Ultimately, in terms of your decisions and operations, you need to make the discernment. Is the drive to grow compromising your ability to tackle GHG footprint? Or is growth enhancing your capacity to reduce those emissions? How else might you change the way you operate to better reflect climate goals while still pursuing profit?

One way that companies are shifting their business model is through the concept of the circular economy. The circular economy, as outlined in Figure 6.2, calls on companies to redesign their product life cycle and reclaim products at end of life, whether that's two days or 20 years after products are sold, salvaging old product content for incorporation into new products. It's a clear and significant sustainable business trend of the past five years.

While circular economy benefits are generally considered to lie in material use versus more direct climate benefits, the concept of reclaiming our products at end of life is powerful enough that it deserves in-depth discussion as well as an understanding of the climate ramifications.

Before we had the circular economy, the Ellen MacArthur Foundation and Circularity conferences to popularize the concept, many of the same concepts were circulating around. An older term that refers to the same notion is "extended producer responsibility" (EPR). Circular economy is more elegant as a term, in my humble

From a linear to a circular economy

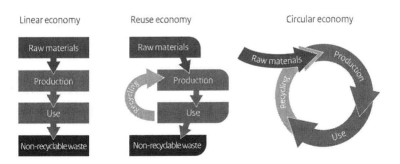

Figure 6.2 Circular Economy.
Source: Government of the Netherlands, Ministry of Infrastructure and Water Management.

opinion, and it is telling as to why that took off where the wonkish EPR did not. Good job, circular branding mavens. In addition to that older term, design for environment (DfE), design for disassembly, and a family of other design practices popularized by the U.S. EPA also predate circular economy, yet hold many practical concepts and practices for the circular economy, like minimizing the points of attachment in product assembly to make disassembly that much easier. Other concepts include using fasteners that can be easily disassembled rather than adhesives and soldering, using a narrower array of materials, and simplifying plastic resins to better allow sorting for recycling.

Here, again, we run into definition issues. How do you define a circular product? Who holds the standard? Ellen MacArthur Foundation, a leader in the space, highlights companies in sectors from apparel to packaging to household goods that reflect the concept, if remaining short of a definition.[3] And that is completely acceptable, as long as there is at least clear definitions of the practices to incorporate and simple metrics like percent of new products composed of used product. Rather than define a product as circular or not circular, and work through yet more certification, for the moment, just work to incorporate the principles into your practices. Companies like PureCycle Technologies can help on the material recycling end,[4] in their case, with plastics. And product certifications like TCO Certified for electronics help encourage circularity.[5]

In addition to circular products, you can also have circular packaging. The Use Reusables campaign was launched by StopWaste for Alameda County in California, and subsequently given the opportunity to go nationwide with U.S. EPA support, to promote reuse of the packaging that most people never see—the pallets, stretch wrap, dunnage (padding in boxes), and other transport packaging which is removed before products go to retail.

How do we know reusables are better than disposables as it pertains to climate? To answer, let's turn where I turn so often—to the LCA oracle. In this case, we understand that reusables are better as shown in Figure 6.3.

Reusables are intuitively understood by most to be better than throwing items away, but that gut feeling is not equivalent to an informed assessment. You could certainly have cases where the

Typical Reusable Tote Application

Application:
- 60,000 reusable totes
- Made with recycled content
- Replacing fiber corrugated fleet
- 6 trips/year
- 8 year tote life
- 22 lb tote load
- 300 mile trip
- Separate backhaul trip
- 90% recycle rate at end-of-life

Reduce Energy Usage by 31%

Reduce Solid Waste by 79.5%

Reduce GHG by 38.3%

Figure 6.3 Reusable Tote.
Source: Orbis Corporation via Reusable Packaging Association.

energy and water taken to reprocess material outweighs the use of virgin material. However, experience and analyses repeatedly prove how disposables are generally not better. When we start making super-low impact single-use packaging out of fallen maple leaves or grass clippings, let's revisit.

Note also that your ability to harness the benefits of reusable packaging all depends on how products are used and transported. For closed-loop transport where you own and/or control the vehicles, reusable packaging can make sense. If you're a manufacturer working through other distributors to get products to retail which then go to individual customers, rather than engineer the reverse logistics or offer return mailing slips, you are likely best off using a minimal amount of compostable packaging.

Even if an LCA indicates that the reprocessing of reclaimed product and packaging has greater impact than use of virgin material, you're not a helpless agent in accepting the results of an LCA. You can work to improve what it's telling you. You can find opportunities to improve the reprocessing footprint, like switching to renewable energy, and change the equation. LCA results often represent the average performance in the industries of your suppliers, upon which you and your suppliers can improve, and if you have a custom LCA using data from your supplier, even better. Look at reprocessing as an opportunity to use renewables, reclaimed water, toxic elimination/substitution measures, and more to improve the profile of your circular product.

For highly manufactured items like electric equipment, it's almost certain that lower GHG impacts lie in reclaiming your product. Circularity, and whatever its next evolution, is here to stay until that distant sci-fi future where either all products are biodegradable or we're 3D printing everything we need out of eco-friendly feedstock and no longer need companies selling products!

Business climate risk: manage and mitigate

> It always seems impossible until it's done.
>
> – Nelson Mandela

Before we go any further, and we have gone quite far, I need to let you in on a little secret. Perhaps it's not so much a secret as it is an omission.

The climate strategy we've discussed thus far focuses on reducing your carbon footprint. That focus starts with the GHG Protocol and continues through CDP, science-based targets, net zero goals, and other business programs. Carbon footprint reduction is the ultimate goal of all of these programs to avoid additional contributions to the climate crisis. However, we already have a climate crisis with which to contend from the legacy GHG emissions that have been already released over the past several decades. You can make a strong argument that your climate strategy should not only focus on footprint reduction, but also place focus on avoiding the disruptions posed by the existing climate crisis. That's alternatively called addressing your *climate risk*. The public sector often refers to it as climate adaptation.

Why isn't climate risk included in these climate programs? In part, I think they rightly focus on the root cause of the climate crisis—GHG emissions. Had we successfully ramped down GHG emissions 20 years ago, climate risk would be much lower. Protocols and programs also evolved in a time when the climate crisis was seen as an issue for future generations. Crisis has since landed in the here and now. However, since addressing risk also closely aligns with business self-interest, I would also guess the programs assume businesses will take care of risk themselves. That allows those programs to focus on the critically needed emissions reductions that are less aligned with self-interest. The public sector is oriented toward risk and adaptation, but the public sector has a different mission than we do as businesses.

In addressing climate risk, we make changes to infrastructure, behavior, and more to make our systems more resilient, better able to respond to extreme weather shocks, and better able to pivot to alternative sources of supplies in the face of supply chain disruption.

Impacts to which to adapt include:

- Wildfire
- Flooding
- Sea level rise
- High heat days
- Drought
- Disease vectors

The climate emergency forces us to gauge where these impacts will hit, in the quest to avoid them. Looking county by county, HIP Investor, an investment advisory firm, created a map of climate risk ratings built around several indicators as shown in Figure 6.4, with different shades indicating different levels of resilience by county.

Why did an investment-oriented firm put this together? As HIP puts it, "both extreme weather events and climate change-induced migration pose the potential to devastate municipal bond issuers' ability to repay their debts." It's not only an issue for the bond market, but also an issue for place-based investments that a company may make.

Figure 6.4 HIP Climate Threat.
Source: HIP Investor, hipinvestor.com.

We're already seeing extensive disaster costs. To help insulate your business from them, consider adding the below to your climate strategy:

- Understand how likely high heat, drought, flooding, sea level rise, wildfire, and/or spread of disease will impact your ability to:
  - Source from the regions that you source from. That includes ability for the region to grow and/or process feedstock as well as ability to transport it
  - Manage facilities in the face of disasters
- Pinpoint actions to address those climate vulnerabilities
  - Identify alternative sources as well as probable price impacts, if sourcing companies are competing for smaller amounts of inputs
  - Identify alternate transportation options, where catastrophe has potential to disrupt existing routes
  - Chart out impact on facilities and retrofits to make facilities more climate resilient. Online retrofit resources, such as those offered by the Resilient Design Institute, may provoke some thoughts[6]

Biodiversity: save two birds with one stone

> There are ethical limits if we are to be human beings . . .
> limits set by the basic rights of diverse species to exist, limits
> on our actions if you respect other beings.
>
>   – Vandana Shiva, author and activist

Biodiversity was introduced earlier in the book as one of the nine
planetary boundaries that has been exceeded, measured by the loss
of plants and animals. Biodiversity is a reflection of the health of
nature-based climate solutions that comprise an impressive portion
of the global climate strategy. If the phrase was used to describe
human institutions, biodiversity actually *is* too big to fail. If our
focus has been on climate, biodiversity is a linked mega-issue worth
visiting.

We've seen apocalyptic and nigh-apocalyptic articles on biodiversity over the years. A recent Cornell study that documented
bird population losses brought the issue back to life,[7] with findings
shown in Figure 6.5. The results of the study aren't much different
than previous Audubon State of the Birds.[8]

More enabling than understanding the state of affairs is understanding the root cause(s). If we can pinpoint those, we can create
an action plan to shift the trends. Researchers say that there "isn't
one single factor that can account for these pervasive losses" of
birds. Sure contributors include:

- Habitat loss (farmland and development)
- Pesticide use
- Insect declines (more on that in a minute)
- Climate change (our perennial, cross-sector, cross-issue issue)
- Direct threats: outdoor cats (your local ferals are definitely a
  factor!), glass skyscrapers

One silver lining, perhaps, is that much of the documented decline
happened from 1970 to 2000, but we could use another positive
data point (I'm rooting for you, 2020s!).

Recently, we also heard from *National Geographic* about plummeting insect populations.[9] That was perhaps a surprise to those who feel
they encounter more than enough insects over the course of their

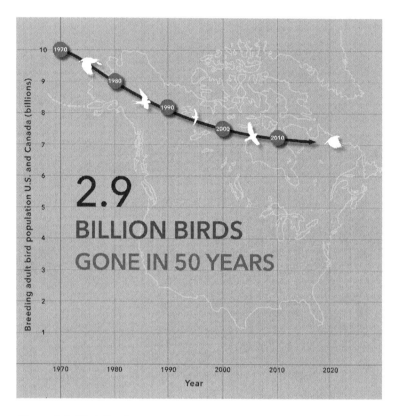

Figure 6.5 Bird Decline.
Source: Jillian Ditner/Autumn 2019 Living Bird magazine, Cornell Lab of Ornithology.

day, but that was the report. Particularly threatened: moths and butterflies, pollinators like bees, and dung beetles and other detritivores.

Similar to "we don't have one single factor that can account for these pervasive losses" with bird life, here we are told it is "death by 1,000 cuts":

- Habitat loss (deforestation and conversion to ag land)
- Pesticide/herbicide/fungicide use
- Climate change

Notice the commonalities between the root cause lists. There is a pathway forward to support the lifeforms with whom we share the planet. That pathway looks similar to what we hear as needed on corporate sustainability fronts, in UN collective efforts, and from grassroots climate groups. And your climate actions play a role.

Dramatically reduce habitat loss

We seek no loss of functional habitats, period. If you're disrupting a functioning ecosystem, providing for the same acreage nearby doesn't fix the disruption that just happened to literally on-the-ground species. Animals and plants need buffer areas and times to naturally migrate. This is relevant in activities like expanding a corporate campus as well as relevant to portions of your supply chain in agriculture, mining, or forestry. Be wary of suppliers expanding acreage, and ask into what types of land they're expanding. Even if these suppliers aren't in your direct Tier 1 relationship, it's worth some investigation into your more distant Tier 2 and 3 suppliers to attempt to get the information. Whether you can use the landscape without disruption is a question worth investigating. Different species have different sensitivities. I'm confident business activity can coexist with natural landscapes, and you can look at the businesses that are already doing it for some inspiration, whether companies incorporating organic agriculture techniques or the select firms working with the Living Building Challenge in their built environment design and construction.

Dramatically reduce use of biocides

Anything that means "kills life" should probably be viewed with suspicion. So much of agriculture is built around use of herbicides and pesticides, in part as past biocide use has unbalanced the natural pest controls that could put pests in check. Shifting away from those substances isn't going to happen overnight. The USDA Organic standard already pushes for biocide reduction and purchasing organic is one measure by which to become more biodiversity-friendly as well as inhibit weeds and pests through substances that more easily break down and pose less of a wildlife risk. However, a great deal of acreage is not organic. That's why a General Mills announcement to convert 1 million acres to re-generative practices[10] was welcome. Note there can be trade-offs in farming techniques, such as the good practice of no-till agri-culture often employing herbicides. If not buying organic, you can source synthetic pesticide-free crops (a portion of the organic standard) and encourage both supplier and any relevant direct op-erations to apply integrated pest management as a means to reduce pesticide use.[11]

Dramatically reduce fossil fuel use

To add to the copious points made on this topic, recall that CDP indicated that 100 companies were responsible for 70% of all emis-sions. Governments give those businesses a license to operate. Their customers give them a market. Businesses aren't in business if there aren't customers. And their employees make decisions on resource use. You do need to also look at who has the power to set the rules to appropriately assign responsibility for reducing that 70% of global emissions, but we all have a role to play in righting the carbon ship. Investments by utilities in renewable energy storage make our job at the business level that much easier, but there are still investments at facilities to make. With those 100 companies making real strides over the next ten years, as well as the hundreds of thousands of companies in their supply chain, we'll be in much better shape.

I can already hear the optimists in the crowd. "Why are you al-ways talking about doing less bad?! Provide a positive and inspiring alternative, rather than push your reduction agenda!"

Well, sometimes you need to refrain from destructive behaviors, and you can extend that into many parts of your life. That said, I hear the concern. Many of you reading this will have explored renewable energy alternatives for your business, have seen pesti-cide-free produce options, and have heard about smart growth and its variants to reduce infringement on wilder places. So, in addition to the tips just offered:

- Do what you can in your business to purchase and/or support responsible options directly. That includes shifting the behavior of your suppliers: incentivize them toward habitat preservation, organic practices, integrated pest management, and clean energy.
- Invest in responsible options where you have fewer direct purchasing options. That might be literally holding equity in other businesses, or it could be donating your "investment" to a great non-profit cause. It could also entail moving your money out of banks that invest in fossil fuels, shifting your checking accounts and 401(k)s to better alternatives.
- Inspire your colleagues, peers, and communities to do the same.

Paint me positive.

The actions to support biodiversity are well aligned with business climate action. Climate change itself is directly implicated in biodiversity losses, and preservation of habitat goes hand-in-leaf with nature-based climate solutions.

Science Based Targets for Nature (SBTN)—as a separate organization from the climate-focused Science Based Targets Initiative, but with a similar intent to use best scientific understanding to protect and preserve living systems—has issued initial guidance for companies seeking to align their operations with the needs of ecosystems.[12] SBTN outlines high-level target categories within which companies should take action, as shown in Figure 6.6.

It is within those "drivers of nature change" where businesses will be called to take action. The list of drivers should look familiar to those who read the trends called out early in this book.

Keep an eye on SBTN developments. We're still in early days, but if it gains as much traction as its climate-oriented sister initiative, you'll want to pay attention.

Onward to avian restoration!

Figure 6.6 Science Based Targets for Nature.
Source: Science Based Targets for Nature, Initial Guidance, Table 2. science-basedtargetsnetwork.org.

Policy: not from the government, still here to help

> If you want to understand the deepest malfunctions of systems, pay attention to the rules, and to who has power over them.
> – Dana Meadows, founder,
> The Sustainability Institute

We've covered a range of technologies and techniques that businesses can use within operations and within the supply chain to help achieve bold climate goals. A portion of your effort should also involve advocacy, influencing incentives and regulations to better enable your responsible climate efforts. The policies we advocate for should track not only business climate action, but, in the best cases, also support aligned efforts in non-business sectors.

Ceres, among the most prominent business networks for sustainability, has created a 2030 Roadmap for business leadership. One of several planks in the Roadmap is Systems Change, calling for public policy engagement of businesses. What they call for as the content of that policy engagement via other planks is shown in Table 6.1.[13]

Table 6.1 Ceres 2030 Roadmap Table

Stabilize the climate	Protect water and natural resources
Build a just and inclusive economy	Strategic planning and execution

If I were to articulate a suite of policies focused on solutions for Stabilize the Climate, the subareas most relevant to businesses include:

- Transportation
- Buildings
- Clean energy finance
- Clean job creation
- Climate risk management

It's worth some analysis to understand the content of the policies to push for, so let's investigate each area more closely. I'll draw on existing analysis by Project Drawdown among other sources.

Transportation

Modeling of transportation sector solutions by Project Drawdown over 30 years yielded the potential GHG savings shown in Figure 6.7.[14]

Total savings is 51 billion tons.[15] Twenty-three percent of sector savings come from electric vehicles. Mass transit is the next highest at 15%, with airplanes next after that at 12%.

In addition to greatest potential GHG savings, it's also important to gauge first costs and the dollar value of savings, as we recommended earlier for your own operations, to be able to gauge the return on investment.

Note I'm using the term "return on investment" loosely. ROI as a formal metric can at times encourage short-term thinking if you have a high ROI threshold to hit. The purpose here is to make

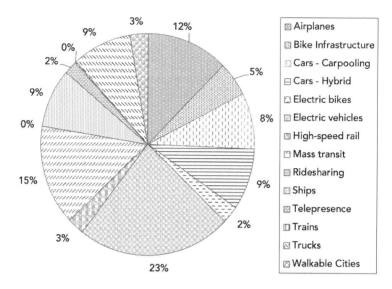

Figure 6.7 Transport GHG Savings Pie Chart.
Source: Made with data from Project Drawdown's Drawdown Update.

sure there is net financial benefit over the lifetime of the solution, whether 3% ROI or 300% ROI, not guarantee 30+%.

As it turns out, many investments save money as well as carbon over time, which is not only a win–win–win, but a no-brainer, as long as you can come up with the initial investment required and/ or use clever financial vehicles when you don't have the required investment on hand. Overly expansive approaches to investment would also compare competing investments that may have zero or negative GHG benefit. However, we are on a mission here! We must not get sidetracked by the allure of investments without real carbon return.

Implementation costs and operational savings are shown in Figure 6.8, showing the pattern of savings versus costs for each technology (column label isn't as important as the general pattern). Negative figures indicate a cost, and positive figures indicate savings.

Many solutions pay for themselves and illustrate a similar pattern. Pour hundreds of billions of dollars in over 30 years, and save trillions. In terms of public investment, not bad. In some cases,

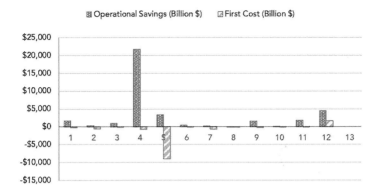

Figure 6.8 Transport Savings/Cost Column Chart.
Source: Made with data from Project Drawdown's Drawdown Update.

the solutions don't generate savings, inviting a conversation around how critical that solution is to solving our problems. However, many public investments don't clearly pay for themselves (roads, parks, military equipment, etc.), and in so many of those cases, they aren't asked to. Those investments often provide a free service to residents and/or solve a public problem, and are not designed to generate revenue. We shouldn't have a double standard, and some climate solutions may well be worth the investment even if the ROI is not there, as they're solving real problems. Speaking of problems, a price on carbon should be applied, as that's not included here and would shift the economics. Carbon-efficient transportation becomes an attractive investment, primarily for the government, which is generally shouldering the costs of transportation infrastructure.

The tall bar near the center of the chart represents EVs. EVs call for the largest individual investment, and cars as a category (including not only EVs, but also hybrids and carpooling) are even larger. EVs also drive the largest portion of savings. At least as impressive, bikes and bike infrastructure have a negative cost. Clearly, there is a cost involved, and I suspect the apparent negative cost stems from factoring in the avoided costs associated with avoided car use.

Policies for which we might petition the federal government include:

- Restore and direct the executive branch to implement the EPA's 2012 requirement for passenger vehicle fleet average fuel efficiency of 54.5 mpg by 2025–2030. This incentivizes hybrids and electric vehicles.
- Improve road and marine freight efficiency through rebate and/or tax incentives. EPA Smartway has a list of technologies and techniques for more aerodynamic road freight that deserve expanded use.[16]
- Advance renewable fuel options for freight. For long-distance road freight, there are electric and fuel cell truck prototypes under development which will need proliferation.
- Help airlines and private jet manufacturers experiment with electric, fuel cell, and renewable biofuel options like hydrogen.
- Invest in electric vehicles, coupled with renewable energy, energy storage, and EV charging infrastructure, as the government invests in the roads that allow EVs and all Vs to serve their transport purpose. This should not be limited to cars: electric bikes, scooters, and skateboards are vehicles suitable for urban, suburban, and small town settings.
- Expand tax credit programs to cover net zero transportation infrastructure to encourage private sector investment.

Buildings

Project Drawdown's modeling of potential GHG savings of building sector solutions over 30 years yielded the results shown in Figures 6.9 and 6.10.[17]

Insulation, LED lighting, heat pumps, and high-performance glass all register as significant opportunities (the taller columns on the chart). Insulation savings so skew the chart, in fact, that it's hard to make out the solutions that are more modest in their savings. Similar to the transportation analysis, we want to look at good return on investments. By this analysis, you get paid to install

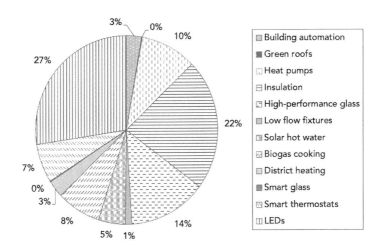

Figure 6.9 Buildings GHG Savings Pie Chart.
Source: Made with data from Project Drawdown's Drawdown Update.

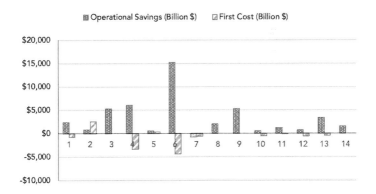

Figure 6.10 Buildings Savings/Cost Column Chart.
Source: Made with data from Project Drawdown's Drawdown Update.

commercial LED lighting and smart thermostats, in the same way bike infrastructure has a net implementation cost of less than zero. The return on heat pumps is impressive, generating nearly 15× the initial cost in savings. Even better, low-flow water fixtures generate 400× savings!

U.S. policy should:

- Phase out incandescent lighting, with select exemptions, and replace with LEDs.
- Work with states to boost insulation levels in building codes.
- Encourage expanded use of heat pumps to replace old HVAC equipment, where appropriate.
- Encourage low-flow water fixtures. Hot water savings also have energy and GHG implications.

In general government should:

- Invest in solutions that don't pay for themselves, where the GHG benefit is significant.
- Invest in solutions that do pay for themselves, where individuals and companies are not acting quickly enough. For those that would like to see government operating with more business savvy, this is a great opportunity to make public investments that yield a return.

Finance

> Governments around the world . . . need to undertake massive climate infrastructure projects, both to protect against physical risk and to deliver clean energy. These challenges will require creative public-private partnership to finance them, as well as better disclosures.
>
> – Larry Fink, BlackRock CEO

In that investment analysis, don't forget to apply a $50+/MTCO_2E$ price on carbon!

Carbon pricing must be part of the solution, on the order of $50–$100/ton. The U.S. government, via the Interagency Working Group on the Social Cost of GHG, set the "social cost of carbon" at $51/ton in February 2021.[18] However, that cost is insufficient to meet social cost. Modeling by Stanford University researchers

(2015) and NRDC/University of Cambridge (2012) suggests that a price on carbon of \$220–\$266/ton is required as an upper bound to ensure costs are covered.[19] A more recent study across countries found a *median* social cost of carbon of \$417/ton, significantly higher than those earlier estimates.[20] \$50–\$100/ton is a good start, ratcheting up to real costs over time without unduly shocking the economy.

Under carbon pricing, we would expect oil, gas, and coal producers and importers to pass the costs onto their customers. To visualize the impact on a gallon of gasoline, divide the per ton carbon price by 100. A \$100/ton price would increase the cost of a gallon of gasoline roughly \$1.00. Impacts on low-income families can be mitigated in the same way we have low-income utility assistance programs. Ultimately, signals need to be sent to the market and individuals that there are real costs to combusting carbon-based fuels, and currently no one is paying those costs.

One of the pre-eminent examples of a successful carbon tax is British Columbia's. The Canadian province instituted a price on carbon in 2008. The price started at C\$10/ton in 2008, rising to C\$30/ton in 2012, adding an extra seven cents per liter of gasoline.

British Columbia required that the tax be revenue-neutral. As a result, while revenues from the tax have gone up, income and corporate tax rates have declined. The province has, or at least had, the lowest personal income tax rate in Canada, and one of the lowest corporate tax rates in North America. Meanwhile, British Columbians saw their fuel usage drop by 16%, while per-person consumption in the rest of Canada rose 3%. All while British Columbia's economic growth outpaced the rest of the country, with GDP per capita rising by 1.75% versus 1.28% for the rest of Canada. GDP as an indicator is problematic, but it is an economic activity indicator. The positive developments explain why a 2012 poll found 64% of British Columbians supported the carbon tax. Canada has since implemented a nationwide price on carbon, beginning at \$20/MTCO$_2$E in 2019 with intent to rise to \$50. Globally, 70 jurisdictions, representing about 20% of global GHG emissions, have put a price on carbon.[21]

In addition to pricing carbon, *it is critical to eliminate fossil fuel subsidies*. In May 2019, the International Monetary Fund calculated that the United States spent $649 billion on fossil fuel subsidies in 2015.[22] Only a portion of that is direct expenditures, and much of that figure has to do with avoided revenue like tax incentives. However, taking their number at face value, that number compares with a $599 billion expenditure by the Pentagon, which is on the order of two-thirds of the U.S. discretionary budget (that is, the amount of budget that is not entitlements like Social Security and Medicare). Redirected fossil fuel subsidies and carbon pricing revenues could be redirected to advance climate solutions.

A final recommendation would have been to advocate to impose a moratorium on oil, gas, and coal extraction on federal lands. However, the Biden administration did just that in January 2021. The rationale is that federal assets should not be contributing to the climate crisis where avoidable. It's conceivable that future generations will need fossil fuels and it would be unwise to deplete those resources when we have viable alternatives.

Clean job creation

> Some people don't like change, but you need to embrace change if the alternative is disaster.
>
> – Elon Musk, Tesla CEO

We will have new industries replacing the old. Investments by the United States should focus on new industrial sites within the U.S. Manufacturing site development should focus in areas hit hardest by the contraction of the fossil fuel industry:

• Native American reservations
• Appalachia
• Cities devastated by the withdrawal of manufacturing jobs
• Other coal, oil, and gas-producing communities

Training and workforce development should then be applied in order to support workers to get into new industries. This helps employers to have a larger pool of qualified workers. Placement is more complex than simply training potential employees, as emerging businesses need to tap markets and drive sales, but it's a good first step. And at times there's a mismatch of both skills and income. A pipefitter who's been making good money fitting oil industry pipes will want to make similar income, whether transferring direct skills to water/wastewater or being retrained into clean energy industries.

Climate risk management/adaptation

To help avoid excessive future costs to our built environment from extreme weather and other climate shocks, new building and rebuilding in known flood- and fire-prone areas should either:

1. only be allowed with requirements to incorporate natural building, disaster-proofing, and resilient building techniques relevant to the specific area and micro-climate, or
2. come with a written agreement that the owners and developers involved forego FEMA disaster relief money, given the rebuild risks to taxpayers without disaster-proofing techniques.

It should be a requirement for government housing funds that this guidance be followed (and in part it already is). Disaster-proof building techniques include the following:

- In flood-prone areas, incorporate floating homes, homes on stilts, first floor and basement level flooring made of moisture-resistant materials, and raised mechanical and electric panels.
- In fire-prone areas, incorporate ceramic and earthen material walls, ember exclusion design on roofs, fire-safe deck and gutter material, and non-combustible siding.

Climate risk management is a form of national security, whether we look at the impacts of extreme weather events, dislocation and forced migration, availability of water, or other likely impacts. As a national security risk, the resources of the Pentagon and the Armed Forces should be deployed to mitigate and reverse the climate crisis. Specific applications:

- Option for soldiers to work in tidal marsh regeneration, reforestation, riparian zone restoration, and other habitat improvement projects that promote climate adaptation and resilience.
- Install large-scale renewable energy systems coupled with electric vehicles to reduce dependence on foreign oil.
- Provide brush clearance around electricity utility lines in fire-prone areas in the West.
- Build seawalls, where appropriate, with the Army Corps of Engineers.

A Civilian Climate Corps has been proposed by the federal government as an alternative, and we will see to what extent it manifests. Whether through the military or an alternate pathway, federal investments into climate resilience are critical.

The climate crisis touches on so many issues. The actions I have illustrated aren't all the answers for the moment, and as we move forward, our needs will evolve. As we get further into implementation, unforeseen problems could arise where our approaches need to be adjusted. What we know is that mass mobilization of all sectors in the face of climate crisis is well worth the undertaking, for the prosperity of us all.

Success on climate will take real investment from all sectors as well as mass mobilization. What we've learned from the 2020–2021 coronavirus pandemic is not only that businesses can pivot with agility, shifting products, and services to meet the moment, but also that countries can mobilize quickly to address a perceived catastrophic threat. We expect deliberation in a democracy, which is generally healthy, but takes more time than other governance models. Yet, even with that, the U.S. Congress managed to find $2+ trillion for unforeseen pandemic expenses in a matter of weeks. Imagine what Congress could do in the face of the threat of the climate crisis, if demonstrating real leadership and will.

Notes

1 Doughnut Economics Action Lab, "About Doughnut Economics", Doughnut Economics Action Lab, 2021. https://doughnuteconomics.org/about-doughnut-economics

2 Tess Riley, "Just 100 Companies Responsible for 71% of Global Emissions, Study Says", The Guardian, July 10, 2017. https://www.theguardian.com/sustainable-business/2017/jul/10/100-fossil-fuel-companies-investors-responsible-71-global-emissions-cdp-study-climate-change

3 Ellen MacArthur Foundation, "Case Studies", Ellen MacArthur Foundation, 2021. https://www.ellenmacarthurfoundation.org/case-studies

4 Stacy Cook, "Innovations in Recycling", National Geographic, January 2020. https://www.nationalgeographic.com/science/2020/01/partner-content-innovations-in-recycling/

5 TCO Certified, "Criteria Designed for Driving Sustainable Development", TCO Certified, 2021. https://tcocertified.com/criteria-overview/

6 Resilient Design Institute, "Resilient Design Strategies", Resilient Design Institute, 2020. https://www.resilientdesign.org/resilient-design-strategies/

7 Gustave Axelson, "Vanishing: More Than 1 in 4 Birds Has Disappeared in the Last 50 Years", Cornell Lab of Ornithology, Autumn 2019. https://www.allaboutbirds.org/news/vanishing-1-in-4-birds-gone/

8 U.S North American Bird Conservation Initiative (NABCI), "State of the Birds 2014 Report", Cornell Lab of Ornithology, 2014. https://archive.stateofthebirds.org/state-of-the-birds-2014-report/

9 Douglas Main, "Why Insect Populations Are Plummeting—And Why It Matters", National Geographic, February 14, 2019. https://www.nationalgeographic.com/animals/2019/02/why-insect-populations-are-plummeting-and-why-it-matters/

10 AGDAILY Reporters, "General Mills to Advance Regenerative ag on 1 Million Acres", AGDAILY, March 5, 2019. https://www.agdaily.com/news/general-mills-regenerative-ag/

11 University of California Agriculture and Natural Resources, "What Is Integrated Pest Management (IPM)?", University of California, 2013. https://www2.ipm.ucanr.edu/What-is-IPM/

12 Science Based Targets Network, "Initial Guidance for Business", Science Based Targets Network, September 2020. https://sciencebasedtargetsnetwork.org/resources/guidance/

13 Ceres, "Roadmap at a Glance", Ceres, October 7, 2020. https://roadmap2030.ceres.org/roadmap-glance

14 Project Drawdown, "Sector Summary: Transportation", Project Drawdown, 2021. https://www.drawdown.org/sectors/transportation

15 Project Drawdown, "Drawdown Update", Project Drawdown, March 2020. Use Minimum Scenario. http://www.drawdown.org
16 U.S. Environmental Protection Agency (USEPA), "SmartWay", USEPA, 2021. https://www.epa.gov/smartway
17 Project Drawdown, "Sector Summary: Buildings", Project Drawdown, 2021. https://www.drawdown.org/sectors/buildings
18 Lorraine Woellert and Zack Colman, "Biden Hikes Cost of Carbon, Easing Path for New Climate Rules", Politico, February 26, 2021. https://www.politico.com/news/2021/02/26/biden-carbon-price-climate-change-471787
19 John Wihbey, "Understanding the Social Cost of Carbon – and Connecting It to Our Lives", Yale School of the Environment, February 12, 2015. https://www.yaleclimateconnections.org/2015/02/understanding-the-social-cost-of-carbon-and-connecting-it-to-our-lives/
20 Ricke, K. et al. Country-Level Social Cost of Carbon. *Nature Climate Change* **8,** 895–900 (2018). https://doi.org/10.1038/s41558-018-0282-y
21 Government of British Columbia, "British Columbia's Carbon Tax", Government of British Columbia, 2019. https://www2.gov.bc.ca/gov/content/environment/climate-change/planning-and-action/carbon-tax
22 International Monetary Fund (IMF), "Climate Change: Fossil Fuel Subsidies", IMF, 2019. https://www.imf.org/en/Topics/climate-change/energy-subsidies

Chapter 7

Put it all together

> We must be rooted in ourselves and our practice . . . remember
> that Right Action comes only from Right Understanding.
> – Thich Nhat Hanh

Time for action!

I want to leave you with not only a menu of actions from which
you can drive real change on climate change, but a process through
which to determine which actions to implement and determine
what is their sequence.

The range of projects a company might consider in a comprehensive climate program is vast. Where do you decide to put your
focus? When helping businesses work through the considerations,
I look through several lenses:

Build the team

- Convene an internal group to further design the company climate + sustainability vision.
- Commit staff time to climate data collection and stakeholder
  engagement.

Understand supplier and customer needs

- What are they planning to do, now and in the future?

DOI: 10.4324/9781003191544-8

Identify market trends (validate those in this book and look beyond)

- What relevant developments have there been?
- What shifts are you seeing in government policies, industry associations, product choices, and supply chain opportunities?

Survey employees

- What do they care about?
- What issues are they seeing?

Engage leadership

- What is the vision?
- What have they/you tried in the past, and what did they/you learn from that experience?

Analyze peer/competitor climate actions

- Look at the priorities and actions of businesses in your industry.

Analyze what climate leaders (all industries) are doing

- If your industry has been relatively inactive and/or you're the first mover (less likely these days, but still possible if your field is small), peer benchmarking isn't likely to be helpful. In that case, it's helpful to understand how advanced businesses in other sectors are responding to dangers and opportunities.

Identify climate impacts

- Work through the GHG accounting process offered in this book.

In the collective, completion of these tasks helps to provide a strategic scan of how and where to focus. The result of the multimodal effort is less of a SWOT analysis (Strengths-> Weaknesses-> Opportunities-> Threats) and more of an understanding of the business ecosystem. Clif Bar calls its ecosystem framework the Five Aspirations.[1] Dr. Bronner's calls it The Cosmic Principles.[2] No matter what you call it, it represents those aspects that are material to your business. Employees are clearly key. John Mackey, head of Whole Foods Market, once said employees are the most important part of their ecosystem. Leadership, peer companies, and the array of resources flowing into the company are all relevant to both climate strategy and climate performance.

By looking at your business through those various lenses, you touch all the different aspects of your business, and all the various systems within which your company is embedded, as shown in Figure 7.1. If you have an existing pathway through which you investigate all those aspects and systems, then no need to adopt yet another checklist, and more power to you.

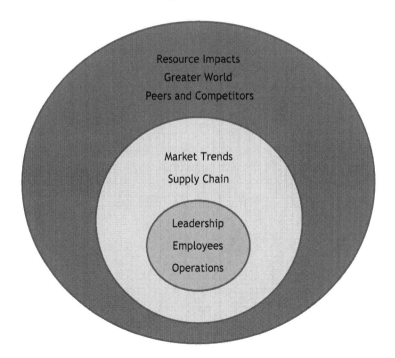

Figure 7.1 Business Ecosystem Aspects Circles.

In looking through those lenses, after you develop the array of projects to launch to get on a better footing, there is still the question of how you prioritize.

In supporting a health insurance company, our team was responsible for managing an array of energy, water, waste, and procurement projects, making decisions on which projects to advance and in what sequence. We ended up with four prioritization criteria, as shown across the top of Table 7.1.

This list of criteria incorporates our basic considerations.

- How much benefit do we get?
- How easy will it be?
- How much does it cost up front?
- What type of return do we get on our investment, return in dollars and beyond?

You might certainly have different criteria. You could incorporate the extent to which strategic partnerships are advanced, extent to which you alleviate key pain points and other criteria that are germane to your business at the moment. If only using two criteria, try plotting projects on a two-by-two matrix and make a heat map like that in Figure 7.2 with the usual guidance: medium-gray (green, if it was in color) means go, dark gray (red) means no go. Those who are aggressive drivers may want yellow (the light gray areas) to mean go very fast, though my guidance is to think more carefully about where to invest money and effort when in the yellow zone.

Table 7.1 Prioritization Table

	Magnitude of impact	Ease of implementation	Total investment	NPV
Projects				

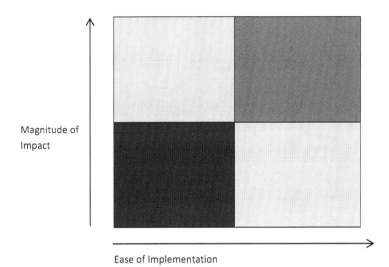

Magnitude of
Impact

Ease of Implementation

Figure 7.2 Prioritization Matrix.

In the prioritization of actions among several criteria, you can quantitatively weight each criterion to score each proposed project. You can also qualitatively weight each criterion to decide which projects to launch, so short of applying numbers, discuss among team members which are most important and why. In any event, you should find assurance that you've crafted a solid approach to advancing your climate program through this process.

Application of those lenses to develop and prioritize projects is inherently a stakeholder-driven process, without biasing the results toward any specific project types. Yet there are explicit goals and projects which we know need to come out of that process for climate action. Customization is needed for your specific circumstance, based on that stakeholder feedback, yet there are commonalities for all businesses to embrace.

Go climate positive

No matter whether you want to call it climate positive or carbon negative, the direction is clear, polarity issues notwithstanding.

Your business should be removing carbon dioxide from the air as long as we're above 350 ppm. More traditional purists may want to dial back to pre-industrial 280 ppm, but our planetary boundary friends and I will take 350 for now. To do that, try these:

Leadership: set science-based targets

- *Procurement goal of 100% renewable electricity* by the 2025–2030 timeframe. Some would push back on me and say it needs to be 2025 and no later, given this is one of the easier first steps. However, I see potential for supply shortages and availability issues if all our commercial and industrial uses, after efficiency, are demanding renewable sourcing. Rather than create incentives to be dishonest, I'd offer a little flexibility.
- *Reduce operational GHG emissions (facilities and fleet) 50+%* between 2020 and 2030. No offsets! This is an actual reduction of your emissions through the strategies listed in this book.
- *Dramatically reduce supply chain GHG emissions.* Following the logic of operational emissions, this would also be 50% reduction, as it should be the goal for the operations of the companies comprising your supply chain. However, given you have less control, the consensus among the SBT crowd has been that you can ratchet down the ambition and the required amount of reduction. Reducing GHG/unit produced in the supply chain is also an option, rather than an absolute reduction.

Operations and procurement: double down on energy efforts

The sequence of events for reducing fossil fuel use is:

- Invest in supply chain redesign to avoid unnecessary energy needs.
- Invest in efficiency in facilities and fleets.
- Install clean energy.
  - Solar
  - Wind
  - Geothermal building systems

- Anaerobic digestion/organic waste to energy
- Other place-based options: tidal, small hydro
- Purchase clean power through utility, where local utility offers it.
- Explore Power Purchase Agreements (PPAs) to (1) have others develop renewables on your facilities, own the system, and sell you the electricity, allowing you to avoid the capital expenses of first cost and/or (2) potentially invest in renewables off-site. The Renewable Energy Buyers Alliance can be helpful in increasing your PPA understanding, where on-site renewables are not an option.
- Purchase Renewable Energy Credits (RECs). This doesn't put new renewables on the grid, in simply buying credit to claim renewable energy from existing sources, but at least sends a market signal for renewables.
- Purchase carbon offsets from high-quality projects as your last resort, after you've made concerted effort with the above.

Other department-specific climate tactics

Whether your work involves financing fossil fuel projects, selling refrigerants, making foods that could end up in landfill, or managing large data centers, there are many tactics that different company divisions can use:

- IT. Get carbon-free websites if you do not already have them. Hosts like AISO.net make that possible. Incorporate data center efficiency and renewable procurement, if not already in place. Data center performance has been an active area of investigation in the tech sector.
- Finance. Screen your actively managed investments to remove coal, gas, and oil. Apply an internal price on carbon.
- Research and development. Innovate and reformulate product content using lower carbon materials.
- Logistics. Capture product at end of life for reuse in new product. Incorporate freight efficiency techniques and shift to more carbon-efficient sea and rail modes where possible, until electric and/or fuel cell road freight is an option.

- Community relations. Work with cities on building decarbon-
ization and used product collection programs. Help augment
their recycling and compost collection systems, where end-of-
life capture isn't an option.

The specifics depend on your situation and where your largest climate impacts lie.

Have some standards

- Take the B Impact Assessment to gauge how close you are currently to achieving B Corp status. Understand what B Corp
status asks of you.

Apply life cycle assessment

- Conduct an initial screening-level LCA of your core products. As LCA can be a significant investment, short of full
LCA, there are screening techniques and hot-spot analyses
you can do to pinpoint your most probable opportunities for
improvement.

There are heightened expectations on what a brand must do to
make the world a better place. If your brand is not already a climate
leader and does not change, it will not survive the next ten years!

Call to action

> One of the biggest things I've learned in more than a decade
> of this work is that you really can make the world better in any
> sector—in nonprofits, in business, or in government. It's not
> a question of one sector struggling against another . . . Today
> business is a key part of the equation.
>
> – Pierre Omidyar, eBay founder

One approach, necessary if not sufficient, through which companies
keep committed to climate solutions is to have a chief sustainability

officer—or at least someone embodying that role—on the leadership team to channel the global vision into wise decision-making. Another approach is to become a B Corporation, though B Corporation is an expression of the underlying culture that's already present, rather than a magical certification that suddenly makes you a good company. That said, there's space to co-evolve, as B Corp principles influence how employees act, and allow the like-minded to use the status as a stake in the ground to move the company forward.

One understated promise of this book was to provide unconventional insights for business success on climate. One of the last unconventional insights I'll offer is that conventional insights have their place. Understanding how business decisions have been made in the past and the conclusions you would come to without a sustainability lens is critical understanding to be able to shift those decisions into a better direction. Without knowing where advocates for other company needs are coming from, it's challenging to constructively address their concerns.

We owe it to ourselves—and to most of post–Ice Age existence, really—to make this decade the Climate Sanity decade. Whether you interpret that to mean sane climate strategy in the face of the crisis, or to mean making adequate progress to keep those of us who care about the issue sane, it doesn't matter. Breakthrough climate success throughout the business community will make things easier down the road. The complementary issues of water use, biodiversity, and toxics are clearly important, not to mention other Sustainable Development Goals vying for your attention. The synergy of climate is that it has direct impacts on water use, is a significant part of the stress on biodiversity, and as we saw, the natural solutions that are critical for climate success also have benefits of habitat preservation and enhancement. You're well on your sustainability way through intelligent climate strategy.

What the climate sanity intention also provides is a deeply rooted *purpose* for us to follow. Psychologist Mihaly Csikszentmihalyi, who popularized the concept of "flow" as a state of optimal experience, observes that "a good life consists of more than simply . . . enjoyable experiences. It must also have a meaningful pattern, a trajectory of growth."[3] That is, random happiness doesn't deliver truly optimal living. It is purpose that provides this meaningful pattern that leads us to our best selves.

My emphasis is making sure not only that you have a purpose, but that your purpose is aligned with what the world needs. You can find purpose in pursuing destructive ends. Anyone with a real moral compass will reject that situation once they're aware of what they're doing, but sometimes through distractions and slow shifts, your inner frog can find itself in an uncomfortably warm pan, forcing you to make a decision where you never would have wanted to choose between the options. In climate positivity lies an opportunity for realignment of your purpose toward noble ends. The Business Roundtable's Statement on the Purpose of a Corporation[4] underscores the fundamental commitment of a business to all its stakeholders. And climate affects them all.

Focus on purpose.
Craft robust climate strategy.
Drive decisive and dramatic climate action.
Go climate positive.

Notes

1 Clif Bar & Company, "The Five Aspirations", Clif Bar & Company, 2020. https://www.clifbar.com/stories/the-five-aspirations/
2 Dr. Bronner's, "The Cosmic Principles", Dr. Bronner's, 2020. https://www.drbronner.com/about/
3 Mihaly Csikszentmihalyi, Official Facebook Page, Mihaly Csikszentmihalyi, 2021. https://www.facebook.com/pg/mihaly.csikszentmihalyi/posts/?ref=page_internal
4 Business Roundtable, "Statement on the Purpose of a Corporation", Business Roundtable, September 2020. https://opportunity.businessroundtable.org/wp-content/uploads/2020/09/BRT-Statement-on-the-Purpose-of-a-Corporation-September-2020.pdf

Index